TIME AND STRATIGRAPHY IN THE EVOLUTION OF MAN

A Symposium Sponsored by the
DIVISION OF EARTH SCIENCES
NATIONAL ACADEMY OF SCIENCES
NATIONAL RESEARCH COUNCIL

October 16, 1965
WASHINGTON, D. C.

PUBLICATION 1469
NATIONAL ACADEMY OF SCIENCES
NATIONAL RESEARCH COUNCIL
WASHINGTON, D. C.
1967

Available from
Printing and Publishing Office
National Academy of Sciences
2101 Constitution Avenue
Washington, D.C. 20418

Library of Congress Catalog Card Number: 67-60011

Preface

ONE of the continuing demands of science is the proper blend-
ing of the new with the old. In any scientific field, growth is
usually sporadic, occurring on different fronts at different times.
Fresh discoveries and sophisticated tools lend enchantment to the
new, and, as frontiers shift, traditional areas of science may be
temporarily eclipsed. When a traditional scientific area fades
from the limelight in this way, some may misinterpret this tem-
porary decline of interest as a decline in importance. Actually,
such declines are rare. More often, challenging problems remain,
which some continue to study and others later rediscover.

New techniques and discoveries in the growing areas of a science may, however, contribute important keys to the solutions of
persistent and fundamental problems. Integration of such new
findings into the existing body of knowledge in a science requires
evaluation of the new in the light of the old. Rarely in the history
of science has a new body of knowledge in an established discipline
or have new methods and tools entirely replaced the traditional.
Moreover, in many fields, particularly in the historic aspects of
the natural sciences, traditional principles of observation and
analysis are essential both to the proper evaluation of new findings and to the sound growth of knowledge and understanding.

Current enthusiasm for geophysics and geochemistry appears

to have left some with the impression that taxonomy of fossils is a closed, if not completed, book, and that the new techniques of dating have made it possible to replace detailed field study of stratigraphic relationships with a hierarchy of numbers. Despite the existence of these views, few would deny the importance of obtaining an accurate geologic picture of a fossil locality or of carefully differentiating the taxonomic characteristics of fossil specimens. Similarly, correlation of the fossil and stratigraphic records of different localities, whether on land or in cores from beneath the sea, is recognized as essential to completing the evolutionary history. These activities are fundamental and traditional enough to merit periodic illustration and reiteration of their central position in the study of the earth itself and of the evolution of life upon it. The Symposium on Time and Stratigraphy in the Evolution of Man was held on October 16, 1965, to provide such a review.

The papers that follow discuss some of the principles of paleontology. While the subject is the evolution of man, the focus is upon the fossil evidence, deciphering the stratigraphic record, progress in absolute dating, and the significance of these factors in the interpretation of the evolution of the human brain. The story of the unraveling of man's evolution illustrates the way in which paleontology, stratigraphy, and modern techniques in geophysics and geochemistry are being joined in the process of finding and relating the pieces that make up this prehistoric record. In addition, the unique character of human evolution calls for a substantial contribution from the social sciences if we are to achieve an adequate understanding of the differentiation and growth of human traits and behavior.

The Symposium was organized at the request and under the aegis of the Division of Earth Sciences of the National Research Council. M. King Hubbert, Chairman of the Division of Earth Sciences, served as chairman of the Symposium. The Division is indebted to the distinguished speakers and discussants for their enthusiastic participation. It wishes also to thank the Wenner-Gren Foundation and the National Science Foundation for their financial support, which made it possible to hold the Symposium and to publish these proceedings. The Division is grateful to the Carnegie Institution of Washington for permitting the use of Root Hall for the Symposium.

Charles B. Hunt
William L. Straus, Jr.
M. Gordon Wolman

Contents

NATURE OF THE PROBLEM AND THE EVIDENCE   1
         William L. Straus, Jr.

Discussion: Chronometric Dating and Taxonomic Relationships   17
         T. Dale Stewart

Discussion: Relationships and Trends in Hominid Evolution   22
         J. T. Robinson

HOMINID-BEARING DEPOSITS OF OLDUVAI GORGE   30
         Richard L. Hay

ABSOLUTE DATING AND THE HISTORY OF MAN   43
         William T. Pecora and Meyer Rubin

Discussion: Stratigraphic Correlations and the Pleistocene Epoch   56
         Cesare Emiliani

Discussion: Application of Fission Track Dating to Anthropology   62
         Robert L. Fleischer

MAN AND NOVELTY   65
         Loren C. Eiseley

Discussion: Brain, Behavior, and Slow Time   80
         Charles D. Aring

TIME, STRATA, AND FOSSILS:
COMMENTS AND RECOMMENDATIONS   88
         Glenn L. Jepsen

Nature of the Problem and the Evidence

WILLIAM L. STRAUS, JR.
Department of Anatomy
Johns Hopkins University

M AN, the genus Homo, taxonomically is a member of the order
Primates. More specifically, he is a member of the subfamily Homininae of the family Hominidae. The Hominidae, with
the Pongidae and the Hylobatidae, the families of the anthropoid
apes, constitute the superfamily Hominoidea.*

The reconstruction of man's phylogeny is peculiarly difficult
because of the scarcity of the necessary fossil material; the habits
and habitats of Primates do not favor their preservation as fossils.
Thus, in contrast to most other mammals, the direct or fossil evidence for primate and hence for human evolution is relatively
scanty and largely incomplete, too frequently consisting of mere
fragments such as jaws or even only teeth. This often has induced
too sanguine an application of the Cuvierian principle of correlation
of parts in attempts to reconstruct entire animals from unsuited
fragments. This is not to deny the validity of the principle of correlation in many instances, but it is largely invalid for Primates
when it is based solely on such parts as isolated jaws and teeth.

*It should be noted that some students regard the superfamily Hominoidea
as comprising more than three families; thus, the controversial fossils
Parapithecus and Oreopithecus are sometimes placed in their own separate families, the Parapithecidae and the Oreopithecidae.

In addition to the anatomical uncertainties, a major problem of human evolutionary studies relates to determination of the ages of the fossils. This involves, above all, relative dating, i.e., the sequential arrangement of the fossils in time, which would aid in determining their phylogenetic relationships. In addition to relative dating, however, absolute dating is greatly to be desired as it would enable estimation of evolutionary rates, not only for the different lines of the hominid radiation but also for the different parts of the body, notably the brain (at least with respect to its size) and the structures primarily concerned with the development of an erect bipedal posture.

Present evidence clearly indicates that the emergence and subsequent evolution of man took place during the Pleistocene epoch. The available fossils come from both the northern and southern hemispheres—in the northern, from both Asia and Europe, in the southern, from Africa. This necessitates better correlative dating, at least relative if not absolute, especially between the two hemispheres, but also between the two involved parts of the northern hemisphere. Without such data, we can only indulge in guessing. Finally, there is the question of when man arrived in the western hemisphere. The answer involves at least dating relative to that of the Old World, preferably absolute dating.

I shall now attempt to present a brief outline of the known fossil record of human evolution, noting the major problems associated with identification and posing questions related to the stratigraphy, correlations, and the significance of dating.*

Let us begin with those fossil hominids termed the Australopithecinae, commonly dubbed the man-apes of South Africa. Most of them come from the Transvaal, but the most recent finds of these creatures have been made in Tanganyika (now Tanzania). These animals are undoubted members of the family Hominidae, but their precise phylogenetic relationship to man remains uncertain. Most students today regard this group as directly ancestral to man; but this is disputed by others, like myself, who regard the australopithecines as a side line of hominid evolution. The solution depends not only upon anatomical considerations but

*For more detailed information concerning the morphology of the fossils considered in this paper, the reader is referred to the following books: Boule and Vallois (1957); Clark (1962, 1964); Comas (1960); Coon (1962); Kraus (1964); Martin and Saller (1957); Montagu (1960); Piveteau (1957); and Koenigswald (1962b).

upon better dating, especially dating relative to undoubted fossils of Homo both north and south of the equator.

The first australopithecine was discovered in the Union (now the Republic) of South Africa at Taung in 1924. During the 1930's and 1940's a number of additional specimens were unearthed at several localities. The specimens fall into two groups. The geologically older forms—from Taung, Sterkfontein, and Makapansgat—which are the more human, are generally termed Australopithecus africanus, in the vernacular, simply Australopithecus (Figure 1). The geologically younger less human forms—from Kromdraii and Swartkrans—are generally termed Australopithecus robustus, in the vernacular, Paranthropus (Figure 2). Morphologically the australopithecines have (1) skulls that are basically simian but that exhibit a number of hominine or manlike characters, the skulls of Paranthropus being the more simian; (2) an essentially human type of dentition, although the two species differ in some respects; and (3) limb bones that indicate that they had achieved a definite if imperfect erect bipedal posture and locomotion. Whether they actually manufactured primitive tools from stone and other materials such as bones, teeth, and horns remains in dispute. In size of brain, estimated in terms of cranial capacity, they scarcely surpass the existing great apes. In fact, the average brain size of both Australopithecus and Paranthropus, approximately 500 cc, is no greater than that of the gorilla, although it is somewhat larger than those of the chimpanzee and orangutan (Tobias, 1963, 1964; cf. Robinson, 1961). In modern man, the normal adult range is from about 1,000 to over 2,000 cc, with approximate racial averages of from 1,250 to 1,525 cc; hence, his average brain size is nearly three times that found in the australopithecines (cf. Martin and Saller, 1957).

The precise dating of the two groups of South African australopithecines remains uncertain. Kurtén (1960, 1962), on the basis of faunal evidence, regards Australopithecus as contemporaneous with the Cromerian (Günz-Mindel) interglacial and Paranthropus as contemporaneous with the Mindel (Elster) glaciation, hence both as Middle Pleistocene. On the other hand, Oakley (1964), using stratigraphy, dates the three Australopithecus sites as Upper Villafranchian, thus as Lower Pleistocene; and the two Paranthropus sites as Basal Middle Pleistocene. These different datings can well lead to different phylogenetic interpretations. (Various charts and graphs showing time, stratigraphic, and evolutionary relationships appear in other papers in this volume.)

Drawings of fossil hominid skulls considered in the text. All are reduced to approximately one eighth natural size.

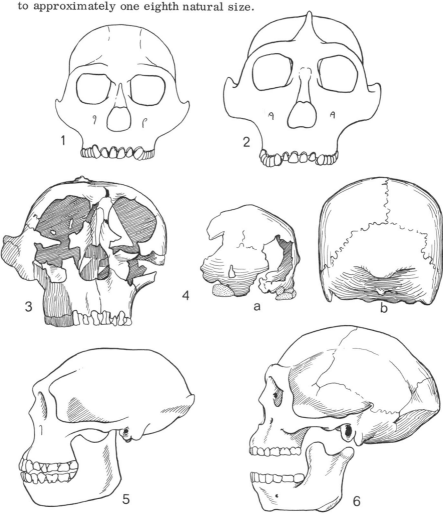

FIGURE 1. Australopithecus (Australopithecus africanus); front view. (After Robinson, 1963; redrawn.)

FIGURE 2. Paranthropus (Australopithecus robustus); front view. (After Robinson, 1963; redrawn.)

FIGURE 3. Zinjanthropus (Australopithecus robustus); front view. (After Leakey, 1959; drawn from a photograph, Figure 9, p. 289.)

FIGURE 4. a. Late adolescent Homo habilis (specimen M.N.K.II) from Olduvai Gorge, and b. Adult modern man (Homo sapiens sapiens); back views. (Drawn from a photograph kindly supplied by Dr. L. S. B. Leakey.)

FIGURE 5. Java man, Pithecanthropus IV (Homo erectus erectus); side view. (After Clark, 1964; redrawn.)

FIGURE 6. Peking man, Sinanthropus (Homo erectus pekinensis); side view. (After Clark, 1964; redrawn.)

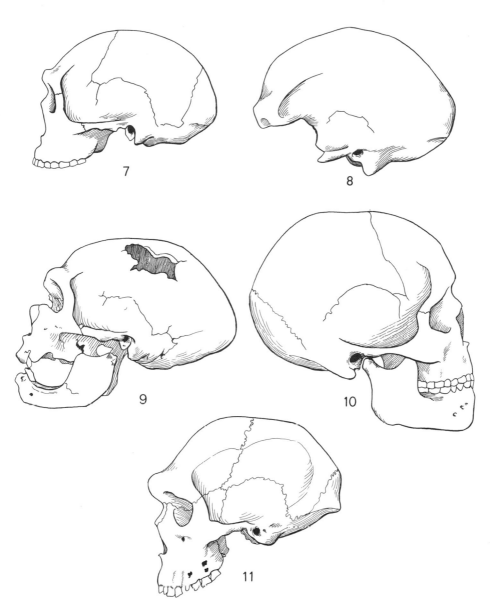

FIGURE 7. Steinheim man (Homo sapiens steinheimensis); side view.
(After Clark, 1962; redrawn.)

FIGURE 8. Ehringsdorf man; side view. (After Clark, 1962; redrawn.)

FIGURE 9. Classic Neanderthal man (Homo sapiens neanderthalensis) from
La Chapelle-aux-Saints, France; side view. (After Clark, 1962; redrawn.)

FIGURE 10. Modern type of man (Homo sapiens sapiens) from Combe-
Capelle, France; side view. (After Clark, 1962; redrawn.)

FIGURE 11. Rhodesian man (Homo rhodesiensis or Homo sapiens rhodesiensis) from Broken Hill; side view. (After Montague, 1960; redrawn.)

Consideration of the hominid fossils, australopithecines and others, recently discovered at Olduvai Gorge, Tanganyika, is of prime importance here. They are the subject of considerable controversy at the present time. Before considering them, however, it is necessary briefly to describe the Olduvai stratigraphy. The strata pertinent to our problem have been termed Beds I and II. Bed I, the older, as originally defined, rests on top of a basalt flow. It in turn is covered by Bed II, which is thus of younger origin. In 1959, Louis and Mary Leakey discovered an australopithecine skull at about the middle of Bed I (Leakey, 1959). They named it Zinjanthropus boisei, but it is now generally regarded as a specimen of Australopithecus robustus and hence a Paranthropus (Figure 3). In size of brain it also is australopithecine, with an estimated cranial capacity of 530 cc (Tobias, 1963). It was associated with primitive stone tools of the type called Oldowan, and a tibia and fibula. Subsequently, at a lower level of Bed I, they uncovered some adult and juvenile skull and limb bones. They too were associated with Oldowan stone artifacts. Since that time, additional hominid remains have been recovered by the Leakeys from both Bed I and Bed II (Leakey and Leakey, 1964). The upper part of Bed II yielded an incomplete cranium resembling those of Homo erectus erectus of Java, originally termed Pithecanthropus; it was associated with more advanced stone tools of the Chellean type. Other hominid remains in Beds I and II have been variously referred to either Homo or Australopithecus.

As noted above, in addition to the Zinjanthropus skull, other hominid remains have been recovered from the lower part of Bed I. They belong to a relatively small-brained creature with an estimated cranial capacity of about 680 cc, less than 100 cc greater than the current maximum estimate for the australopithecines (Tobias, 1964, 1965a). These remains, together with other specimens from Beds I and II (Figure 4a), recently have been diagnosed as human by Leakey et al. (1964), who have referred them to a new hominine species, Homo habilis, a species they regard as the maker of the Oldowan stone tools. This classification has aroused controversy. Some reject the assignment of the fossils to the genus Homo, regarding them as actually australopithecine; others also reject the distinctive designation H. habilis but on different grounds (see Campbell, 1964, and Robinson, 1965, 1966). Some see a resemblance between H. habilis and controversial jaw fragments discovered in 1949 at Swartkrans, in the Transvaal; these Swartkrans fragments were originally termed Telanthropus

capensis, later assigned by Robinson (1961) to Homo erectus, and
are regarded by others as a subspecies of Australopithecus africanus (Campbell, 1964). Tobias (1965a) believes that "at least in
East Africa, and, probably, too, in South Africa, H. habilis and
Australopithecus spp. were sympatric and synchronic." Hence he
concludes that "since they are contemporary with H. habilis, the
australopithecine populations represented by the actual fossils
recovered to date are clearly too late—and possibly slightly too
specialized—to have been in the actual human line, unless we are
to postulate a polyphyletic origin of the Homininae at varying times
from australopithecine stock." However, he believes that "the
closeness of morphology between H. habilis and Australopithecus
africanus points strongly to a common ancestry in the Upper Pliocene or the very beginning of the Pleistocene" (also see Tobias,
1965b, 1965c, 1966). So the biological controversy rages.

Accurate absolute dating of the Olduvai beds is obviously of the
greatest importance. The Bed I deposits, which yielded Zinjanthropus and H. habilis, have been dated as approximately 1.75 million
years B.P. by the potassium - argon (K - Ar) method (Leakey et al.,
1961) and as 2.03 million years B.P. by the fission-track method
(Fleischer et al., 1965)—quite a close agreement. The validity of
this particular K - Ar date has been questioned, however (Straus
and Hunt, 1962), because although the K - Ar dating indicates a great
time break between Beds I and II (Leakey et al., 1961), this is not
supported by either the paleontological (Koenigswald et al., 1961)
or the stratigraphic evidence (Hay, 1963).* Moreover, one K - Ar
study of the basalt underlying Bed I (Koenigswald et al., 1961) has
yielded a date that is actually less than that secured for Bed I
itself. Other K - Ar studies of the basalt, however, label it as at
least as old as, and probably older than, Bed I (see Curtis and
Evernden, 1962; Hay, 1963; Oakley, 1964). So the dating contro-
versey rages.

To know the ages of the Olduvai hominids relative to the ages
of the South African hominids is of prime importance. Kurtén

*A study of Olduvai Gorge, published after the present paper was written,
denies the existence of a major break between Beds I and II (Leakey, 1965).
It states, however (p. 4), that "The lower and upper parts of Bed II are
separated by a break of considerable magnitude. This can be established
by geological evidence and is also represented by a major faunal change.
. . .The view is taken here that Bed II may be divided into three parts.
The lower series, which is lacustrine and fluviatile, belongs geologically
with Bed I."

(1960, 1962) has concluded that the Paranthropus remains from South Africa are contemporaneous with the Mindel glaciation of Europe, which by any estimate makes them much younger—perhaps 1 million years or more—than the ages currently assigned to the Paranthropus (i.e., Zinjanthropus) of Tanganyika. If Paranthropus is as highly specialized as some of us think (Straus, 1959; Robinson, 1961; Tobias, 1965a), one may well question whether it lingered on in Africa at the same time as more advanced forms, including man, for a million years or more. This example emphasizes the need for better dating, preferably absolute, but at least relative.

Turning now to our own genus, Homo, or man, and leaving aside disputed and problematic H. habilis, we come to the earliest generally accepted human species, H. erectus. According to the current orthodox view, H. erectus evolved into our own species, Homo sapiens. Its earliest known representative is H. erectus erectus, in the vernacular, Pithecanthropus or Java man, the first specimen of which was discovered in 1891. A number of other specimens were collected from 1934 to 1941 (Figure 5). Thus, parts of seven skulls and several femora are now available. The skulls, although showing numerous primitive features, as would be expected, are far more human than those of the australopithecines, and the thigh bones are indistinguishable from those of modern man. Hence, there is excellent reason for assuming that Pithecanthropus had attained a fully erect bipedal posture. In size of brain, however, Java man comes close to being overlapped by the gorilla, its adult range extending from 775 to 900 cc, with an average of about 860 cc. No tools have been found in direct association with any of the Pithecanthropus remains, but it seems likely that the slightly younger Patjitanian primitive stone implements were made by later members of that group (Oakley, 1964). Most of the Pithecanthropus specimens have been assigned by Kurtén (1962) to the Middle Pleistocene at the time of the Mindel glaciation, with an estimated age of about 500,000 years (Oakley, 1964). This age has been obtained by correlation of the associated fauna with that from another location for which a K - Ar dating of 490,000 years B.P. has been secured (Koenigswald, 1962a). Kurtén (1962) regards the infant pithecanthropine skull from Modjokerto, Java, as older, ascribing it, on a faunal basis, to the time of the Cromerian interglacial. Jaws of a pithecanthropine, vernacularly termed Atlanthropus, were discovered in Algeria in 1954. Primarily by stratigraphic correlations, the jaws have been assigned an early Mindel date (Biberson, 1961).

Hence it would appear that by this date H. erectus erectus was
rather widely distributed, inhabiting, at the least, both Asia and
North Africa.

Between 1927 and 1937, in a cave at Choukoutien near Peking,
China, the remains of some 59 individuals were uncovered, including five more or less complete skulls, of a hominine fossil
commonly termed Sinanthropus, or Peking man. This creature
is undoubtedly a variety of pithecanthropine, somewhat more advanced than the Javan form, and is properly termed Homo erectus
pekinensis (Figure 6). His limb bones bear testimony to a fully
erect bipedal posture. The brain of Sinanthropus was considerably
larger than that of Pithecanthropus, the adult endocranial capacity
ranging from 915 to 1,225 cc, with an average of approximately
1,040 cc. Peking man also seems to have made considerable cultural progress. His associated stone tools resemble those from
the Patjitanian beds of Java. But there is good evidence that he
had attained controlled use of fire and that he was a cannibal.
Indeed, these are the earliest known evidences of these human
cultural phenomena. Sinanthropus evidently was a descendant of
Pithecanthropus, and this is in line with his assigned dating. On
the basis of both floral (pollen and spore) and faunal analysis,
Kurtén and Vasari have dated Sinanthropus as contemporaneous
with the Mindel II or Elster II glaciation of Europe (Kurtén, 1959;
Kurtén and Vasari, 1960). Because the age ascribed to the Elster,
as determined by a K - Ar dating, is about 360,000/years, Kurtén
(1959) has attributed a similar age to Peking man. Thus, on
Kurtén's dating, Sinanthropus would be some 130,000 years younger than Pithecanthropus and approximately the same age as
Paranthropus of South Africa.

Before we leave the Far East, we should take note of Solo man,
sometimes termed Homo soloensis. Represented by parts of 11
skullcaps (but no faces) and 2 tibiae, he was found in 1931 and 1932
at Ngandong, Central Java, with stone and bone tools of a fairly
advanced type. Solo man is regarded as an advanced member of
the pithecanthropine group, although in brain size (average about
1,100 cc, range 1,035 - 1,255 cc) he had progressed no further
than Peking man. His age seems, on stratigraphic and cultural
grounds, to be late Pleistocene; but more-precise dating is lacking.

The most ancient known European hominine fossil is the famous
Heidelberg lower jaw, discovered in 1907 in the sandpit of Mauer,
Germany. It is commonly referred to the species H. erectus, but
this specific assignment can be questioned. The jaw shows certain

peculiar characters, yet it is undoubtedly human. The teeth, although rather large, are distinctly human. Unfortunately, subsequent excavations at the Mauer sandpit have failed to yield any
other part of the skeleton. The jaw has been referred to the
Cromerian interglacial, with a date, determined relatively on a
stratigraphic and faunal basis, of over 500,000 years B.P. (Oakley,
1964). This would make it about as old as or even slightly older
than the earlier South African australopithecines (if we accept
Kurtén's dating) and quite as ancient as the oldest Javan Pithecanthropus. The implications of this ascribed dating are so important
for phylogenetic analysis that the need for greater precision is
obvious.

Other important European finds of early fossil men that require
better dating are the Swanscombe and Steinheim skulls.

The Swanscombe skull, which consists of most of the cranium
but lacks the face, was discovered, two fragments in 1935-1936
and another in 1955, at Swanscombe, England, along the Thames
River. In cranial capacity, which is about 1,325 cc, and gross
cerebral morphology, as shown by its endocranial cast, it falls
well within the range of modern man. Since it resembles a modern
skull in many ways, the Swanscombe skull was formerly classified
as an example of modern man, Homo sapiens sapiens. Recent
studies, however, have revealed certain Neanderthaloid characters
(see Ovey, 1964). Therefore, like the Steinheim skull, to which it
bears some striking resemblances, it is now generally regarded
as a so-called early Neanderthaloid, or, as one might designate
it, a Homo sapiens steinheimensis.

The Steinheim skull, discovered two years earlier, in 1933, at
Steinheim, Germany, is almost complete, lacking only the lower
jaw (Figure 7). Although its reported cranial capacity is some
200 cc less (approximately 1,100 cc), its braincase resembles
that of Swanscombe man. Hence it also is a so-called early Neanderthaloid, a H. sapiens steinheimensis.

Both skulls have been referred to the Holsteinian (Hoxnian;
Mindel-Riss) interglacial, the Swanscombe skull by both faunal
and archeological correlations, the Steinheim skull by faunal correlation alone. An inferred date of about 250,000 years B.P. has
been assigned to Swanscombe man and one of about 200,000 years
B.P. to Steinheim man (Oakley, 1964). The desirability of pro-
curing more-precise dating of these earliest known representatives of H. sapiens is evident.

Attention must also be paid to the fragments of two human

skulls discovered in 1947 at Fontéchevade, France. The more
complete skull undoubtedly had a cranial capacity of more
than 1,400 cc, well within the range for modern man. Without
going into details here, it must be noted that these fossils have
been the subject of considerable dispute. To put it simply, are
they the remains of so-called early Neanderthaloids, or are they
actually the earliest known representatives of our own subspecies,
H. sapiens sapiens? They have been assigned to Eemian (Riss-
Würm) interglacial, with age estimates, inferred on theoretical
grounds, ranging from 70,000 years to perhaps 150,000 years
(Oakley, 1964). Again, the need for more-precise dating is quite
obvious.

Mention must also be made of the Ehringsdorf braincase found
near Weimar, Germany, in 1925 (Figure 8). This cranium is
usually regarded as a so-called early Neanderthaloid (by some,
however, as an actual Neanderthal). Referred to the Eemian interglacial, it has recently been assigned an age of between 60,000 and
120,000 years by dating the associated travertine by the proactin-
ium-thorium method. (Rosholt and Antal, 1963). This would place
it within the age range ascribed to the Fontéchevade skulls. But
more-precise dating would certainly be welcomed. The Ehringsdorf cranial capacity is approximately 1,450 cc, about the same
as that of Fontéchevade. It appears, therefore, that by the time
of the Eemian interglacial the human brain had attained its
present size.

We now come to more recent times, to consider a relatively
well-known fossil man—actual Neanderthal man, Homo sapiens
neanderthalensis. The type specimen was discovered in 1856 in
a cave overlooking the Düssel River, Germany, just three years
before the publication of Darwin's On the Origin of Species by
Means of Natural Selection. Actually, however, a far more complete skull had been found on the Rock of Gibraltar in 1848, but it
was not identified until many years later. Since then, numerous
remains of classic Neanderthal man (the term "classic" being
appended to distinguish actual Neanderthal man from the earlier,
so-called early Neanderthaloids and other "Neanderthaloid" specimens) have been discovered at many localities in the eastern
hemisphere north of the equator, i.e., in many countries of Europe
and the Near East, thus extending from the Atlantic Ocean eastward to Iran and Uzbekistan (and possibly in the Far East and
North Africa as well).

Space does not permit discussion of the morphology of the classic

Neanderthal in detail. The cranium (Figure 9) has a peculiar form, described as bun-shaped. There are prominent browridges, and a true chin is usually lacking. But the enclosed brain was exceptionally large, the adult cranial capacity ranging from about 1,200 to well over 1,600 cc. Indeed, the average capacity apparently was at least 1,450 cc, equal to or even surpassing that found in some of the largest-brained groups of modern man. Despite earlier claims to the contrary, the endocranial casts suggest a brain in no way inferior to that of modern man. This conclusion is supported by the quality of the associated stone tools, comprising the Mousterian culture, and the indisputable evidence that the classic Neanderthal buried his dead, even with some ceremony.

Classic Neanderthal man was formerly and still is, popularly, pictured as but semierect—as almost hunchbacked, with head bent forward, standing or walking with bent knees and flat, inverted feet—and thus but incompletely adapted to bipedal locomotion. Recent restudy of Neanderthal skeletons, however, has revealed that this reconstruction of classic Neanderthal posture is incorrect; it resulted from overlooking the deforming arthritis that was a common Neanderthal affliction and from misinterpreting certain characters of his trunk and limb skeleton (Straus and Cave, 1957). There is nothing, therefore, to support the common supposition that classic Neanderthal man was other than a fully erect biped.

It once was thought that classic Neanderthal man was a direct lineal ancestor of modern or sapiens man (Hrdlička, 1927, 1930; Weidenreich, 1940, 1943, 1947). This concept has generally been abandoned, and most students of the problem now believe that classic Neanderthal man represents a line of evolution collateral to that of modern man—a separate, essentially gerontic terminal line of human evolution that was displaced and extinguished by the modern type of man (Howell, 1951, 1952; Koenigswald, 1962b; Clark, 1964). Their common ancestor would be a so-called early Neanderthaloid, a H. sapiens steinheimensis. Brace (1964), however, has recently revived the concept that the classic Neanderthals were the immediate, direct ancestors of modern man. Thus, at least for the moment, the precise position of H. sapiens neanderthalensis in human phylogeny is in dispute. The dispute involves the groups of Neanderthaloid fossils discovered between 1925 and 1934 in the caves of Tabūn and Skhūl on Mount Carmel, Palestine (Israel). In many respects the fossils exhibit a mixture of classic Neanderthal and modern human characters, which has given rise to two interpretations directly related to the two theories of classical Neanderthal man's place in phylogeny. For some persons, the Mount Carmel population represents race mixture between Neanderthal and modern man. However, the two cave populations do show certain differences that have been diversely interpreted. The most Neanderthaloid of all the skeletons was found at Tabūn, the most sapiens at Skhūl. Since it has been claimed that the human remains of Tabūn are slightly older than those of Skhūl, a second school of thought believes that the Mount Carmel population was in the process of evolution from actual or classic Neanderthal man into modern or sapiens man (Brace and Montagu, 1965). However, whereas the dating of Tabūn seems quite acceptable; that of Skhūl is not (Oakley, 1964). Absolute dating of the Skhūl site, therefore, is most desirable, because it could well contribute greatly to a solution of the problem of whether the Skhūl remains represent race mixture or a step in the evolution from Neanderthal to modern man.

All the undoubted classic Neanderthal fossils have been dated as either Eemian interglacial or Würm glacial. A few absolute ages have been secured by radiocarbon dating of the associated deposits. In other instances, dates have been estimated by correlation with other deposits of which the actual ages have been measured. These methods have yielded dates ranging between about 30,000 and 70,000 years B.P. (Oakley, 1964).

Undoubted modern man, H. sapiens sapiens, first appears in Europe during the Würm glaciation. Although numerous specimens of that period have been recovered, their precise dating still remains uncertain (see Oakley, 1964). Nearly all the assigned dates have been obtained by correlation of the source deposit with one whose actual age has been ascertained, hence, secured by inference. The dates range between 12,000 and 34,000 years B.P., with most of them in the range 12,000 to 17,000 years B.P. A few direct determinations of the age of the source deposit, as by the radiocarbon method, have been made; they give ages from about 10,500 to about 26,500 years B.P. Estimates made on theoretical grounds have yielded similar ages, from 12,000 to 30,000 years B.P. The highest of these figures, notably that of the skeleton from Combe-Capelle (Figure 10), in the Dordogne region of France, dated 34,000 years B.P., would make modern man contemporaneous with classic Neanderthal man, at least in Europe. For there is no doubt that the Combe-Capelle skeleton is that of Homo sapiens

sapiens, more specifically, in all probability a member of the Cro-Magnon race. The bearing of these discoveries and their assigned dates on the evolutionary relationship of classic Neanderthal and modern man is obvious. Hence, more-precise dating of these early remains of modern man, preferably absolute dating, is one of the greatest importance.

A primitive type of man lingered on in South Africa until relatively recent times. He is represented by the Rhodesian skull and limb bones found in 1921 at Broken Hill, Northern Rhodesia (now Zambia), and the Saldanha skull found in 1953 in the vicinity of Hopefield, near Cape Town. The Rhodesian skull (Figure 11) possesses truly enormous browridges and a primitive, rather Neanderthaloid face, combined with an essentially sapiens braincase. The limb bones resemble those of modern man. The Saldanha skull is much less complete, comprising only the skullcap and a mandibular fragment; the skullcap, however, attests to its close affinity with Rhodesian man. The endocranial capacities are quite similar, measuring about 1,280 cc in Rhodesian man and about 1,250 cc in Saldanha man. Opinions differ respecting the taxonomic allocation of these specimens. They have been classified as H. erectus; or as a separate species, Homo rhodesiensis; or as a subspecies of our own species, Homo sapiens rhodesiensis. They are undoubtedly to be dated, from stratigraphic and cultural associations, as Upper Pleistocene. No absolute dates are available, but by the inferred correlation an age of about 40,000 years has been assigned to Saldanha man and one of about 30,000 years to Rhodesian man (Oakley, 1964).

Finally, we come to the question of when man arrived in the New World. All skeletal remains of early man in the western hemisphere are clearly of the modern type, H. sapiens sapiens. It is now generally believed that man was present in North America at the time of the last glacial maximum (see Hunt, 1965). Moreover, some persons are of the opinion that he arrived in the western hemisphere even earlier than that time (see Carter, 1957). What is really needed is absolute dating, or at least stratigraphic evidence for dating the earliest sites, as well as stratigraphic evidence showing the route by which man arrived in the New World.

This over-all, necessarily abridged, presentation of our knowledge of fossil men notes some of the problems involved in the interpretation of their ages, morphological evolution, and lines of descent. The importance of precise dating for their solution has been emphasized.

REFERENCES CITED

Biberson, P., 1961, "Le Paléolithique Inférieur du Maroc Atlantique," Service des Antiquités du Maroc, 17, 544 (cited by Oakley, 1964).

Boule, M., and H. V. Vallois, 1957, Fossil Men, Dryden Press, New York (English translation of Les Hommes Fossiles).

Brace, C. L., 1964, "The Fate of the 'Classic' Neanderthals," Current Anthropol., 5, 3-43.

Brace, C. L., and M. F. A. Montagu, 1965, Man's Evolution, Macmillan and Company, New York.

Campbell, B., 1964, "Just Another 'Man-Ape'?" Discovery, 26, 37-38.

Carter, G. F., 1957, Pleistocene Man at San Diego, Johns Hopkins University Press, Baltimore, Md.

Clark, W. E. Le G., 1962, History of the Primates: an Introduction to the Study of Fossil Man, 8th ed., British Museum (Natural History), London, 119 pp.

Clark, W. E. Le G., 1964, The Fossil Evidence for Human Evolution: an Introduction to the Study of Paleoanthropology, 2nd ed., University of Chicago Press, Chicago, 200 pp.

Comas, J., 1960, Manual of Physical Anthropology, rev. ed., Charles C Thomas, Publisher, Springfield, Ill.

Coon, C. S., 1962, The Origin of Races, Alfred A. Knopf, Inc., New York.

Curtis, G. H., and J. F. Evernden, 1962, "Age of Basalt Underlying Bed I, Olduvai," Nature, 194, 610-612.

Fleischer, R. L., P. B. Price, R. M. Walker, and L. S. B. Leakey, 1965, "Fission Track Dating of Bed I, Olduvai Gorge," Science, 148, 72-74.

Hay, R. L., 1963, "Stratigraphy of Beds I through IV, Olduvai Gorge, Tanganyika," Science, 139, 829-833.

Howell, F. C., 1951, "The Place of Neanderthal Man in Human Evolution," Am. J. Phys. Anthropol., 9, 379-416.

Howell, F. C., 1952, "Pleistocene Glacial Ecology and the Evolution of 'Classic' Neanderthal Man," Southwestern J. Anthropol., 8, 377-410.

Hrdlička, A., 1927, "The Neanderthal Phase of Man," J. Roy. Anthropol. Inst., 57, 249-274.

Hrdlička, A., 1930, "The Skeletal Remains of Early Man," Smithsonian Inst. Misc. Collections, 83, 1-379.

Hunt, C. B., 1965, "Quaternary Geology Reviewed," Science, 150, 47-50.

Koenigswald, G. H. R. von, 1962a, "Das absolute Alter des Pithecanthropus erectus Dubois," in Evolution und Hominisation, G. Kurth, ed., VEB Gustav Fischer Verlag, Stuttgart, Germany, pp. 112-119.

Koenigswald, G. H. R. von, 1962b, The Evolution of Man, University of Michigan Press, Ann Arbor (English Translation of Die Geschichte des Menschen).

Koenigswald, G. H. R. von, W. Gentner, and H. J. Lippolt, 1961, "Age of the Basalt Flow at Olduvai, East Africa," Nature, 192, 720-721.

Kraus, B. S., 1964, The Basis of Human Evolution, Harper & Row, Publishers, Inc., New York.

Kurtén, B., 1959, "New Evidence on the Age of Peking Man," Vertebrata Palasiatica, 3, 173-175.

Kurtén, B., 1960, "The Age of the Australopithecinae," Stockholm Contrib. Geol., 6, 9-22.

Kurtén, B., 1962, "The Relative Ages of the Australopithecines of Transvaal and the Pithecanthropines of Java," in Evolution und Hominisation, G. Kurth, ed., VEB Gustav Fischer Verlag, Stuttgart, Germany, 74-80.

Kurtén, B., and Y. Vasari, 1960, "On the Date of Peking Man," Commentat. Biol., Helsingf., 23, 1-10.

Leakey, L. S. B., 1959, "The Newly-Discovered Skull from Olduvai: First Photographs of the Complete Skull," The Illustrated London News, Sept. 19, pp. 288-289.

Leakey, L. S. B., 1965, Olduvai Gorge, 1951-61, Vol. 1: A Preliminary Report on the Geology and Fauna, Cambridge University Press, New York, 118 pp.

Leakey, L. S. B., J. F. Evernden, and G. H. Curtis, 1961, "Age of Bed I, Olduvai Gorge, Tanganyika," Nature, 191, 478-479.

Leakey, L. S. B., and M. D. Leakey, 1964, "Recent Discoveries of Fossil Hominids in Tanganyika: at Olduvai and near Lake Natron," Nature, 202, 5-7.

Leakey, L. S. B., P. V. Tobias, and J. R. Napier, 1964, "A New Species of Homo from Olduvai Gorge," Nature, 202, 7-9.

Martin, R., and K. Saller, 1957, Lehrbuch der Anthropologie, Vol. 1, 3rd ed., VEB Gustav Fischer Verlag, Stuttgart, Germany.

Montagu, M. F. A., 1960, An Introduction to Physical Anthropology, 3rd ed., Charles C Thomas, Publisher, Springfield, Ill.

Oakley, K. P., 1964, Frameworks for Dating Fossil Man, Aldine Publishing Co., Chicago.

Ovey, C. D., ed., 1964, "The Swanscombe Skull: A Survey of Recent Research on a Pleistocene Site," Roy. Anthropol. Inst. Occasional Publ., 20, 215.

Piveteau, J., 1957, "Primates: Paléontologie Humaine," Traité de Paléontologie, Vol. 7, Masson et Cie, Paris.

Robinson, J. T., 1961, "The Australopithecines and Their Bearing on the Origin of Man and of Stone Tool Making," S. African J. Sci., 57, 3-13.

Robinson, J. T., 1963, "Adaptive Radiation in the Australopithecines and the Origin of Man," in African Ecology and Human Evolution, F. C. Howell and F. Bourlière, eds., Aldine Publishing Co., Chicago, 385-416.

Robinson, J. T., 1965, "Homo 'Habilis' and the Australopithecines," Nature, 205, 121-124.

Robinson, J. T., 1966, "The Distinctiveness of Homo Habilis," Nature, 209, 957-960.

Rosholt, J. N., and P. S. Antal, 1963, "Evaluation of the Pa^{231}/U-$Th^{230}U$ Method for Dating Pleistocene Carbonate Rocks," U.S. Geol. Survey Prof. Paper 450-E, E 108-111 (cited by Oakley, 1964).

Straus, W. L., Jr., 1959, discussion in "The Descent of Man and the Present Fossil Record," G. Heberer, in Genetics and Twentieth Century Darwinism, Cold Spring Harbor Symp. Quant. Biol., 24, 243-244.

Straus, W. L., Jr. and A. J. E. Cave, 1957, "Pathology and the Posture of Neanderthal Man," Quart. Rev. Biol., 32, 348-363.

Straus, W. L., Jr., and C. B. Hunt, 1962, "Age of Zinjanthropus," Science, 136, 293-295.

Tobias, P. V., 1963, "Cranial Capacity of Zinjanthropus and Other Australopithecines," Nature, 197, 743-746.

Tobias, P. V., 1964, "The Olduvai Bed I Hominine with Special Reference to Its Cranial Capacity," Nature, 202, 3-4.

Tobias, P. V., 1965a, "Early Man in East Africa," Science, 149, 22-33.

Tobias, P. V., 1965b, "New Discoveries in Tanganyika: Their Bearing on Human Evolution," Current Anthropol., 6, 391-411.

Tobias, P. V., 1965c, "Australopithecus, Homo Habilis, Tool-Using and Tool-Making," S. African Archaeol. Bull., 20, 167-192.

Tobias, P. V., 1966, "The Distinctiveness of Homo Habilis," Nature, 209, 953-957.

Weidenreich, F., 1940, "Some Problems Dealing with Ancient Man," Am. Anthropol., 42, 375-383.

Weidenreich, F., 1943, "The 'Neanderthal Man' and the Ancestors of 'Homo Sapiens,'" Am. Anthropol., 45, 39-48.

Weidenreich, F., 1947, "Facts and Speculations Concerning the Origin of Homo Sapiens," Am. Anthropol., 49, 187-203.

DISCUSSION

Chronometric Dating and Taxonomic Relationships

T. DALE STEWART
Museum of Natural History
Smithsonian Institution

CONSIDERING the limitations of time imposed on him, Dr. Straus has been able to give a reasonably full account of the fossils pertinent to a discussion of the evolution of man, at the same time pointing out some of the major problems of taxonomy and chronology. In his usual careful fashion he has avoided the semantic and nomenclatural difficulties that beset this subject. On one point, however, I would like to raise a question: Is the present discussion being limited to the genus Homo and to the Pleistocene epoch, as Dr. Straus seems to imply? The title of this symposium includes the phrase "the evolution of man," and at the outset of his paper Dr. Straus quite correctly equated man to the genus

Homo, taxonomically a member of the order Primates and of the subfamily Homininae, etc. Then he stated that "the emergence and subsequent evolution of man took place during the Pleistocene epoch." Yet, in presenting his "outline of the known fossil record of human evolution" (note the use now of the word "human") he began with those fossil hominids termed the Australopithecinae, commonly dubbed the man-apes of South Africa." The reason for bringing in this group seems to be their controversial taxonomic status, because Dr. Straus places himself with the minority of today's students in regarding the australopithecines "as a side line of hominid evolution." Although he does not say that he subscribes to it, he quotes Tobias' statement that "The australopithecine populations represented by the actual fossils recovered to date are clearly too late—and possibly slightly too specialized—to have been in the actual human line, unless. . . ." If we accept this point of view, we are left with the even more controversial juvenile remains from site FLK NN. I* in Olduvai Gorge, the type specimen of the new species Homo habilis, as the main reason for extending the discussion of the evolution of man (Homo) back in time about 2 million years by present physicochemical estimates (more than twice the long-accepted duration of the Pleistocene). However, Dr. Straus simply dismisses Homo habilis as "disputed" and "problematical." As a fellow anthropologist I can understand Dr. Straus's position, even though it might seem a bit inconsistent, because it naturally develops out of the raging biological controversy, to use his characterization. Such controversy usually indicates inadequate but tantalizing evidence.

All this recalls the famous 1950 Cold Spring Harbor Symposium on the Origin and Evolution of Man. One of the important contributions on that occasion was a proposal by Ernst Mayr that fossil and recent hominids be classified in a single genus (Homo) with three species: transvaalensis—to include the australopithecines; erectus—to include the pithecanthropines; and sapiens—to include the Neanderthals and modern man. This proposal was accepted only as far as the two species erectus and sapiens are concerned, as Dr. Straus's usage of the names shows. Back in 1950 no one could bring himself to put the australopithecines under the genus Homo, much less under the species Homo transvaalensis. There is still resistance to the idea. However, the current difficulty in distinguishing between Homo habilis and Australopithecus africanus

*Frieda Leakey Korongo, North, Bed I—Leakey, 1965, p. 102.

makes the following statement by Mayr (1950, p. 118) seem pro-
phetic: "As far as brain size and use of tools is concerned, there
has been apparently a continuous line of development from the
primitive hominids to modern man. Java man (? or ape-man) is
so completely intermediate between South African man and modern
man, and the difference between these two terminal forms so much
a matter of degree, that it seems questionable whether these evolutionary stages justify generic separation. The difference is certainly not equivalent to a generic difference in most groups of
animals."

In view of Mayr's opinion and the fact that the present symposium stresses chronology more than taxonomy, I am sure that no
one objects to extending the range of the discussion backward at
least to the time represented by the bottom of Olduvai Bed I. There
is relatively little evidence available for hominids before that time.
And here I might point out that while Dr. Straus mentions conflict-
ing potassium - argon (K - Ar) dates relative to Bed I and the underlying basalt, he does not seriously question the general order of
magnitude of the reported dates. At a Wenner-Gren symposium
on the Origin of Man, held in Chicago in April 1965, Dr. Evernden
(DeVore, 1965, p. 27) commented on the validity of the 1.76-to-
1.9-million-year Bed I date, for which he was partly responsible.
He said, "As a hard-working geochronologist who has applied
every test and technique that a geochronologist can apply to numerous minerals from multiple samples from the same bed and
many strata in the same sequence, [I] feel that that date is as
secure as any in the entire geological column."

Speaking of absolute, or, to use the term preferred by Dr. Oakley
(1964, p.2), "chronometric" dating, it was not easy for Dr. Straus
to convey in his account of taxonomic relationships the full effect
that the dates made available by such methods as fission track,
K - Ar, and ^{14}C have had on studies relating to human evolution.
When anthropologists interpret undated human remains, they often
have no alternative but to rank them on the basis of morphological
judgments. This process has been disparagingly called morphological or anatomical dating. Chronometric dating already has revealed
the contemporaneity of specimens that, because of their very different appearance, might otherwise have been assigned to an evolutionary sequence. Dr. Straus has cited the example of Australopithecus
robustus and Homo habilis. At the nearer end of the time range I
have had the advantage of working with a Neanderthal, Shanidar I
from Iraq (Stewart, 1959), for which a ^{14}C date (47,000 years ago)

promptly became available. Just knowing that I was dealing with
such a late specimen has been a great advantage in interpreting
the findings.

By contrast, the Neanderthals from the Skhūl and Tabūn caves
at Mount Carmel, Palestine (Israel), found in the early 1930's,
were assigned too great an age, a dating that persisted for 25 years
after their discovery. Up to 1952, Zeuner dated these Neanderthals as from the closing phases of a dry, warm interpluvial, which
was considered to correspond to the European Last Interglacial
stage. In 1957, Howell put them in the Early Last Pluvial. In 1961
Higgs and Brothwell presented evidence suggesting a difference in
age of around 10,000 years, undermining the original concept of
the describers, McCown and Keith (1939, p. 11), that the remains
from both caves were "contemporaneous in a moderately narrow
sense." There is now a ^{14}C date (Oakley, 1964, pp. 304-305) for
Tabūn of about 40,000 years and thus a suggested date for Skhūl
of about 30,000 to 35,000 years. Naturally, the earlier erroneous
dating led to much confusion in the literature regarding the relationship of these Neanderthals to modern man.

Even with good dating it is possible to be misled by the surviving parts of early man. Dr. Straus has complained about the
attempts "to reconstruct entire animals from unsuited fragments,"
particularly isolated jaws and teeth. I think he has good grounds
for being suspicious of such reconstructions, although how invalid
they are is seldom clear. Probably in some cases the bony parts
that have disappeared were stranger looking than we can imagine.
I personally was able to recover and identify the superior ramus
of the pubic bone in three Shanidar Neanderthals. This is a part
of the pelvis that has not survived in any of the other classic
Neanderthals except one from the Tabūn cave. Quite unexpectedly,
all four finds show a condition never seen in modern man, consisting of a vertical thinning of the ramus and a corresponding
enlargement of the obturator foramen (Stewart, 1960). By contrast, the skeletons from the Skhūl cave show the modern form
of pubic bone. In other words, the classic Neanderthals of
Shanidar-Tabūn, dated 40,000 to 60,000 years ago, have an otherwise unknown form of pubis, whereas the less primitive looking
Shkūl people, dated possibly 30,000 to 35,000 years ago, have the
modern form of pubis. The occurrence of two such distinct kinds
of human groups in such a late time period strongly supports the
idea that the modern variety of man, represented about 20,000 to
30,000 years ago in Europe by the Cro-Magnons, developed from

a Skhūl-like rather than a Shanidar-Tabūn-like line. What became of the Shanidar-Tabūn line is still a mystery.

As for man in America, a paper read by Marie Wormington at the International Congress of Americanists, held in Spain in 1964, offered the conclusion that there is nothing as yet from the archeological standpoint to support an antiquity of more than 20,000 years (personal communication). The only serious challenge to this opinion recently has been the finding by L. S. B. Leakey and Ruth Simpson of putative man-made artifacts at considerable depths in a solifluction deposit of Wisconsin glacial age located in the Calico Hills, Manix Lake Basin, California (personal communication). These "artifacts" have not yet been fully accepted as man made by the few authorities who have examined them. Studies are continuing at the site to determine the distribution of the "artifacts;" a very wide distribution, both vertically and horizontally, would favor the view that the flaking is due to soil creep.

REFERENCES CITED

DeVore, P. L., ed., 1965, The Origin of Man, Transcript of Symposium sponsored by the Wenner-Gren Foundation for Anthropological Research, Inc., convened by Sol Tax, University of Chicago, April 2-4, 1965, 152 pp.

Higgs, E. S., and D. R. Brothwell, 1961, "North Africa and Mount Carmel: Recent Developments," Man, 61 (166), 138-139.

Howell, F. C., 1957, "The Evolutionary Significance of Variation and Varieties of 'Neanderthal' Man," Quart. Rev. Biol., 32,(4), 330-347.

Leakey, L. S. B., 1965, Olduvai Gorge, 1951-61; Vol. 1: A Preliminary Report on the Geology and Fauna, Cambridge University Press, New York, 118 pp.

Mayr, E., 1950, "Taxonomic Categories in Fossil Hominids," in Origin and Evolution of Man, Cold Spring Harbor Symp. Quant. Biol., 15, 109-118.

McCown, T. D., and A. Keith, 1939, The Stone Age of Mount Carmel: The Fossil Human Remains from the Levalloiso-Mousterian, II, Oxford University Press, New York, 390 pp.

Oakley, K. P., 1964, Frameworks for Dating Fossil Man, Aldine Publishing Company, Chicago, 355 pp.

Stewart, T. D., 1959, "The Restored Shanidar I Skull," Smithsonian Inst. Rept., 1958, pp. 473-480.

Stewart, T. D., 1960, "Form of the Pubic Bone in Neanderthal Man," Science, 131, 1437-1438.

Zeuner, F. E., 1964, Dating the Past: An Introduction to Geochronology, 4th ed., Hafner Publishing Co., Inc., New York, 516 pp.

Relationships and Trends in Hominid Evolution

J. T. ROBINSON
Departments of Anthropology and Zoology
University of Wisconsin

EVIDENCE now available from fossils concerning the evolution of man has been briefly reviewed by Dr. Straus. He has, quite properly in the circumstances, concentrated on reviewing the evidence rather than giving his particular views about its interpretation. Since he has presented this essentially impartial account, I wish to give very briefly my interpretation and to indicate where new dating would assist in interpreting the evidence. Since there is not sufficient time to document my conclusions I shall necessarily be somewhat dogmatic; for this I apologize in advance.

Long-continued study of the australopithecines has led me to conclude that (1) true man, of the genus Homo as currently understood, sprang from an australopithecine ancestor; and (2) the switch mechanism that shunted the lineage of man off in a new direction, leading to the establishment of culture as an important basis of adaptation, was a change from primarily herbivorous to omnivorous diet.

On the basis of this interpretation there are only two primary lineages in the hominid group. The first and more primitive is that of Paranthropus, the apparently herbivorous, somewhat ape-like australopithecine known from the latter end of the Lower Pleistocene and apparently well into the Middle Pleistocene, by which time the genus Homo was well established. This lineage appears to have died out in the Middle Pleistocene. The second lineage or phyletic line is that of Australopithecus-Homo, australopithecine in its earlier stages and hominine in its later ones. The Australopithecus stage of this line seems to have been confined to the Lower Pleistocene; the Homo portion started at the base of the Middle Pleistocene and has continued to the present.

However, as Pleistocene stratigraphy is in a rather unsettled state, one cannot be sure just where the boundary between the Lower and Middle Pleistocene lies in relation to these two lineages.

On present evidence, however, it seems clear that the earliest known representatives of both lineages come from roughly the same time interval in the later part of the early Pleistocene and that Paranthropus continued to exist in at least two widely separated areas in the Old World after Australopithecus had been transformed into Homo.

Unfortunately almost nothing is known about the stage that preceded that of the australopithecines. It has been suggested that Ramapithecus, a Pliocene pongid from India (which may also include Kenyapithecus from the East African late Miocene), is so good a prospective ancestor for the australopithecines that it should be placed in the Hominidae and regarded as a hominid. The claim has also been made that Ramapithecus is difficult to distinguish from Australopithecus. So few specimens, representing so few parts of the skeleton, are known that one cannot, in my opinion, learn enough about this form to decide whether it belongs in the Hominidae. Nothing at all is known about the locomotor habit or even about most of the skull, because only pieces of upper and lower jaw have been found. On the basis of the small amount of evidence now available, this material can clearly be distinguished from the australopithecines. However, too little is known about Ramapithecus, and the time gap between it and the australopithecine material is far too long to judge with any certainty whether this form could have been ancestral to the australopithecines.

It has also been suggested that Oreopithecus, from the early Pliocene of Italy, from Bessarabia, and apparently also from the late Miocene of East Africa, is an australopithecine ancestor and true hominid. A great deal more is known about this animal than about Ramapithecus, and it is clear that Oreopithecus is not very similar to the australopithecines. It seems hardly possible to regard Oreopithecus as a hominid, especially as brachiation was apparently its means of locomotion. But again, the time gap between Oreopithecus and the australopithecines is much too large for anyone to judge with any accuracy the likelihood that it may have been their ancestor. Oreopithecus appears to have had pelvic features that almost certainly occurred in the australopithecines, but, since we do not know anything of its later evolution, we are not able to judge whether Oreopithecus was changing in this direction.

The hominid group, as now accepted, probably came into existence with the emergence of habitual erect posture in what otherwise was an ape-like creature. That is to say, the creature probably had an ape-sized brain, an ape-like skull, and a herbivorous

diet. Erect posture was probably an adaptation suiting it better to
its largely ape-like way of life and probably had nothing whatever
to do with culture or the possibility of cultural development at that
stage. Paranthropus, it seems to me, represents essentially this
evolutionary stage; it appears to have been a robust herbivore of
the forest verge or open woodland that never developed culture to
a significant level, to judge from available evidence. It habitually
walked erect, though some evidence suggests that perhaps it still
engaged in a certain amount of climbing.

 Paranthropus is quite well known (some 200 specimens) from
South Africa from the end of the early Pleistocene and part way
into the middle Pleistocene. A few specimens from the Olduvai
region suggest that it persisted with little change in that region
from early Bed I to the énd of Bed II times—a period of well over
a million years if the present dates are correct. In my opinion,
the few specimens of Meganthropus from Sangiran, Java, are of
this same genus. Evidently this genus represents a stable adaptation that persisted over a long period of time—how much earlier
than late early Pleistocene is not known. Evidently Paranthropus
was also spread widely in the Old World. In South and East Africa,
as well as in Java, it has been found at the same horizons of the
same sites as a member of the other hominid lineage. The evidence,
which in some cases is explicit and incontrovertible, shows that
members of both hominid lineages simultaneously inhabited the
same region. At Swartkrans, Telanthropus II was found deep in the
solid breccia mass in direct association with Paranthropus material, and in Bed I at Olduvai, Paranthropus (= Zinjanthropus) occurred on the same floor at the same site as Homo habilis material.
The Bed I H. habilis material is, in my opinion, Australopithecus.
The evidence for synchrony at these sites is independent of dating,
unlike other situations in which synchrony is inferred when similar
dates have been obtained for different sites in the same areas. In
East Africa the evidence indicates that Paranthropus coexisted
with the second lineage in both its Australopithecus and its Homo
phases. The South African and the Javanese evidence indicates
that coexistence concerns only the Homo level.

    For economy of hypothésis and because Paranthropus seems to
have possessed the basic features to be expected in a form changing from the ape grade of organization to the hominid grade, it
seems probable that the second hominid lineage sprang from the
Paranthropus line at a more primitive stage than that known at
present. The morphology of Paranthropus and Australopithecus is
in agreement with such a suggestion, except for the excessively

reduced anterior teeth of the latter. However, in earlier stages, these teeth almost certainly would have been larger, because all known earlier fossil primates have larger canines and incisors than Paranthropus.

If, in earlier stages, Australopithecus did indeed have larger anterior teeth, it is of interest to consider what the basis was of the different set of selective factors that shaped the second lineage. Since diet is clearly a major factor in the life of any animal, and since it is clear that a herbivorous diet of one sort or another is the basic dietary type of the higher Primates (other than man, who is an omnivore because meat-eating is a very significant aspect of his dietary regime), it is reasonable to consider a herbivorous diet as a possible factor in the change. Clearly, a form with relatively poorly developed canines and with nails instead of claws would be at a disadvantage as a hunter and meat-eater if he did not have the assistance of tools of some sort. Similarly, more-intelligent forms would be in a better position to cope with the increased difficulties and uncertainties of a predator's life as compared with the life of an herbivore, whose food does not run away from him. If a change to an actively predacious mode of life occurred—and since man is a predator and other higher Primates are not, such a change probably did occur—then natural selection will surely have favored manual dexterity, tool using and tool-making, and improved intelligence. Therefore, within the natural range of variation present in the population at any one time, individuals who were better endowed with such skills and qualities would have an advantage over the less-well-endowed individuals and generally would contribute more genetic material to the next generation. One can thus readily see the basis of the selection pattern that favored the establishment of culture as a very important feature in the Australopithecus-Homo lineage.

There is clearly more to it than that, however. In bad seasons, when food is scarce, primates such as baboons can become predacious. But they revert to their normal diet as soon as conditions improve. Thus, it is obvious that a significant change in diet of this order would not have occurred readily and for no apparent reason. There is, however, considerable geologic evidence that the African continent suffered appreciable desiccation through the Pliocene; the Kalahari is a fossil desert bearing witness to this. With increasing desiccation, some populations of the early Paranthropus type would gradually have come under increased pressure to supplement their diets with animal protein during the latter part of the dry season. Others, living in areas where the natural-

habitat resources did not drop below the minimum level for support of herbivorous forms of the sort here involved, would continue living according to their "old" way of life. Two different
selection patterns would thus have been in operation: one would
have maintained Paranthropus in its essentially original form,
while the other would have favored improved intelligence, improved facility with tools, improved communication, agility, and
gracility. Such conditions must have continued and intensified
over a long period, thus allowing the second set of selection pres-
sures to produce significant change in the affected individuals.
Once the new ecology, behavior, and morphology had become
established as part of a complex adaptation, improvement of the
climate would not have resulted in reversion to the old way of life,
since this adaptation is a particularly powerful one that, in fact,
has allowed man to become the dominant organism on this planet.

On the basis of this hypothesis, one would expect that the fossil
record of the second lineage (Paranthropus-Australopithecus-
Homo) would show an increase in brain size, paralleled by an increasingly modern form of hand, and evidence of improvement in
tool using and toolmaking.

It seems to me that the Olduvai sequence, scanty as it is, is
especially interesting in this connection. In South Africa, from
where the vast majority of known australopithecine specimens
have so far come, Australopithecus appears to have been in an
early stage of this development. There is clear evidence that the
brain was beginning to expand, though the expansion had not yet
gone far, and there is a lot of evidence that Australopithecus was
actively and effectively tool using, but apparently he was not yet
an active and systematic toolmaker in stone. Bed I at Olduvai has
yielded a few specimens that have been placed, with some material from Bed II, in a supposedly new species of Homo, H. habilis.
However, it seems impossible to distinguish the Bed I material
from Australopithecus as known in South Africa. There are some
slight differences, as inevitably there must be in the circumstances,
but all the relevant sorting criteria seem to me to place the Bed I
material in Australopithecus with a rather high level of certainty.
It is possible that the average brain size of these Bed I specimens
was a little larger than in the South African forms, and it seems
clear that the Bed I man was also a regular toolmaker in stone in
the early Oldowan tradition, thus apparently representing an
advanced Australopithecus stage. The hand apparently was still
somewhat primitive.

The Bed II material that has been attributed to H. habilis is, however, rather clearly distinguishable from Australopithecus, whether from Bed I or from South Africa. Average brain volume seems to have increased, because at least one specimen appears to have had a braincase significantly larger than any known for Australopithecus and with a much smaller degree of narrowing of the braincase behind the orbits. However, another fairly small braincase indicates that there was still much overlap in size with the Australopithecus stage. The teeth are reduced in size, and, with this, changes have occurred in the shape and proportion of the lower jaw to produce an internal mandibular contour at present known only in Homo. Also, the associated industry has now reached a more advanced stage, that of developed Oldowan. This is apparently also the stage represented by Telanthropus from Swartkrans, South Africa, where the mandibular characteristics of the Bed II material are present, and the industry is also of the advanced Oldowan stage. This stage corresponds to an early Homo erectus level.

From the top of Bed II has come a fairly complete braincase which clearly has the basic characteristics of Homo erectus of an advanced type, such as is fairly well known from Java and China. The endocranial volume was roughly 1,000 cc, and the associated culture was the very early Acheulean type.

The next stage is indicated by such material as the Swanscombe and Steinheim specimens, which show that the typical H. erectus features were, by Great Interglacial times, being refined toward the modern H. sapiens condition. From here, increasing amounts of material are available, indicating refinement through the Neanderthal stage to the late Palaeolithic peoples, who evidently were essentially of the modern type physically. This change has been accompanied by greater refinement and complexity of the cultural evidence. It is clear that as the Australopithecus-Homo evolution has proceeded physical changes have become less and less important while cultural changes have become increasingly so.

This evolutionary pattern is set out diagrammatically in Figure 1.

There are many places in this story for which improved dating evidence would be welcome, and in a few, such new evidence is badly needed. For example, it would be valuable to know exactly what the time relation of the South African australopithecines is to the Olduvai sequence of Beds I and II. On the assumption that the South African material is much younger than that from Olduvai, a few workers have suggested that neither type of australopithecine is related to the emergence of Homo, though it would seem that

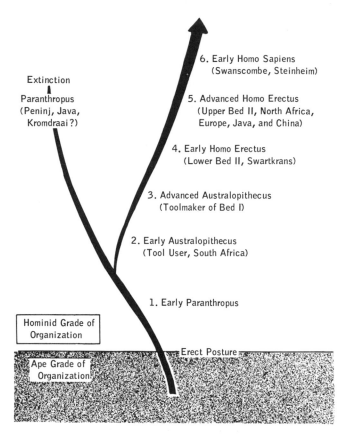

FIGURE 1. Hominid evolution. Stages 3, 4, and 5 are known from Olduvai
Beds I and II: 3—Bed I H. habilis material; 4—Bed II H. habilis material;
5—the so-called Chellean skull from the top of Bed II. Stage 2 is known
from South Africa. It is not known at present whether the South African
material is actually earlier than the Bed I material of Stage 3 or whether
it represents a more slowly evolving local population still in existence
after early Bed I time. The exact time relation of the forms bracketed
under Stage 5 is not altogether clear. The early Paranthropus level
(Stage 1) is unknown as yet. The Paranthropus line is represented at the
level of Stage 3 in Bed I at Olduvai (Zinjanthropus) and perhaps also at
the Stage 4 at Swartkrans. By far the best-known sample of Paranthropus comes from the Swartkrans sites in South Africa, but just what its
time relation is to Beds I and II at Olduvai is not known. Synchronous
presence of both lineages in the same site occurs at the Stage 3 level
at Olduvai, the Stage 4 level in South Africa, and the Stage 5 level in
Java. The time difference between Stages 3 and 5 appears to have been
of the order of 1 to 1.5 million years.

this conclusion is not a necessary consequence of that assumption. However, the somewhat inadequate faunal comparisons possible do not support the idea that the Olduvai material is significantly the oldest. Clearly, reliable chronometric dating would be of great help here.

Similarly, it seems clear that somewhere there must have been a transition from Australopithecus to Homo; but what is the time relation between the Asiatic specimen of H. erectus (Javanese and Chinese pithecanthropines) and that from Europe (Mauer)? On the basis of present evidence, it would seem that the lower Bed II and Swartkrans specimens of H. erectus are the oldest. However, there are some uncertainties here: the age of the Mauer specimen in relation to the African material is uncertain, and some primitive stone artifacts from sites in central Europe may also be from Lower Pleistocene levels. We urgently need to have clarity on these dates in order to pin down the probable area of origin of Homo.

These questions point to a general problem: correlating Pleistocene divisions from one part of a continent to another and from continent to continent. Although the glacial - interglacial sequence based on four major European glaciations and a rather vague earlier Donnau phase is commonly used as a reference frame, there is much uncertainty about details or even major aspects, and its usefulness is somewhat problematic at present. Certainly there is not much clarity about anything earlier than Mindel, as far as the frame of reference goes, and different usages from one author to another are a fruitful source of mis- understanding. Reliable dates would go a long way toward clarify- ing this situation.

One of the major complications about sorting out the evolution of man seems to be that at any one time interval mankind was not represented by a single compact population with a clearly defined level of development. Instead, at any one time there were many scattered, or at least semi-isolated, local populations that were not all exactly the same in their characteristics or level of ad- vancement. This introduces complications that are difficult to unravel without reliable dates. Some of the problems we face are simply a consequence of having insufficient fossil material to answer the questions we are asking. But some of the serious problems stem from inadequate stratigraphy and dating, and in these areas more assistance from stratigraphers and geochronol- ogists and their allies would be most useful and very welcome.

Hominid-Bearing Deposits of Olduvai Gorge

RICHARD L. HAY
University of California

INVESTIGATIONS in Olduvai Gorge, Tanganyika (now Tanzania), illustrate the use of stratigraphic techniques in establishing the relative stratigraphic position, paleoenvironment, and absolute age of hominid remains and artifacts. Pleistocene beds are exposed over a 15-mile length of the gorge, which lies at an elevation of about 5,000 ft in equatorial East Africa. The beds were deposited in a basin possibly ranging from 10 to 30 miles in diameter that lay to the east of Ngorongoro and other volcanoes of the eastern Rift Valley (Figure 1). The maximum thickness of Pleistocene beds exposed at any one place is about 350 ft. The beds contain hominid remains of great antiquity and an unsurpassed sequence of Paleolithic artifacts and occupation sites (for example, Leakey, 1951; Leakey and Leakey, 1964).

The rocks in Olduvai Gorge were described by Reck (1951, pp. 5-19) as a basal series consisting of various kinds of interbedded volcanic and continental sedimentary materials. Reck divided this series into five units, which he called Beds I, II, III, IV, and V; each is a formation consisting of many smaller depositional units. Bed V overlies the older deposits with pronounced angular unconformity and will not be considered further. Pickering (1965) mapped the geology of the gorge and adjacent areas and observed the lateral intertonguing of different sedimentary facies.

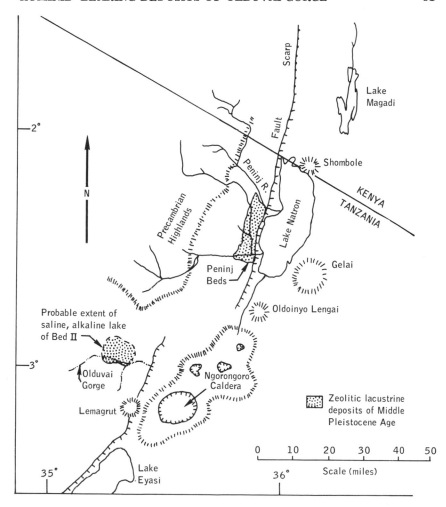

FIGURE 1. Index map of part of East Africa showing locations of Olduvai
Gorge and nearby volcanoes and saline lakes. Zeolitic lacustrine deposits
of Middle Pleistocene age are: the saline - lacustrine facies of Bed II,
Olduvai Gorge, and the Peninj beds to the west of Lake Natron. Distribution of the Peninj beds is taken from Isaac (1965).

Because he found stratigraphic correlation uncertain, he advocated
replacing Reck's vertical subdivision with one emphasizing lateral
facies changes. During the summers of 1962 and 1964 the writer
made a stratigraphic study of the gorge more detailed than those
of Reck and Pickering. Approximately 150 stratigraphic sections
were measured, and numerous key horizons were traced laterally.

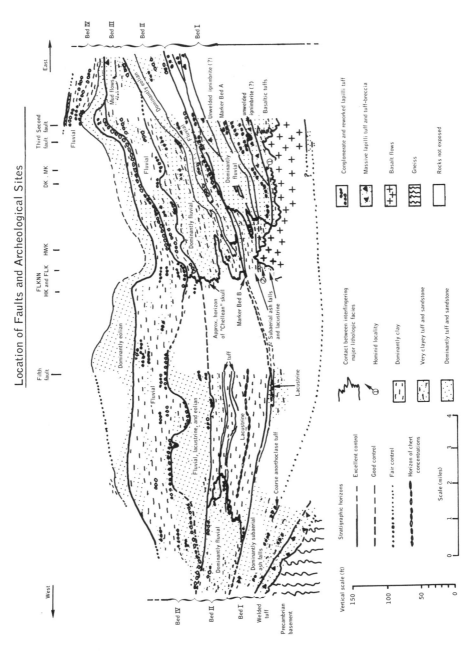

FIGURE 2. Stratigraphy of Beds I – IV along Olduvai Main Gorge, based upon fieldwork in 1962 (Hay, 1963a). Sequence to the west of Site HWK was reconstructed by taking as a datum the upper surface of saline–lake deposits of Bed II.

Fieldwork was supplemented by extensive microscopic and x-ray study of the rocks. Reck's subdivision was found to be generally satisfactory and is continued here with slight modification.

As a result of fieldwork in 1962, the previously accepted stratigraphic framework of Beds I and II was modified in several ways.

1. Lava flows taken as the basal unit by Reck and Pickering were found to be conformably interbedded with trachytic pyroclastic deposits and clays of Pleistocene age and are now considered members of Bed I (Hay, 1963a). Their pahoehoe surface is only slightly weathered and eroded, indicating that the flows were extruded only a relatively short time before the overlying land-laid tuffs were deposited. This discovery aided in resolving the controversy over the absolute age of the flows (see Leakey, 1965, pp. 87-91).

2. Two different tuffs (Marker Beds A and B of Figure 2) of rather similar appearance had been miscorrelated (see Hay, 1963a). Recognition of this error led to clarification of the vertical stratigraphic relations of Beds I and II.

3. A widespread unit of eolian tuff was found within Bed II, allowing further subdivision of the bed. The tuff unit drops progressively in a westward direction, lying close to the top of Bed II near the mouth of the gorge and only 8 ft above the base of Bed II to the west, near site HWK. Recognition of this progressive drop in the position of the tuff unit led to the positioning of fossils and artifacts with respect to marker tuffs within Bed II instead of by measuring their vertical distances above the base or below the top of Bed II.

The results of fieldwork in 1964 substantially modified the writer's earlier interpretation of the stratigraphy and origin of Beds III and IV and the upper part of Bed II. Additional measured sections showed that the thickness of these deposits changes abruptly across several faults (Figure 3), instead of by gradation as the writer had inferred previously (Figure 2). The new data show that faulting in the Olduvai Basin began during the deposition of Bed II and continued intermittently through the deposition of B Beds III and IV.

The paleogeography and geologic history for Beds I through IV can now be reconstructed from the pattern of lithologic facies and measured sedimentary structures such as channel orientations and crossbedding. Below are summarized some of the salient facts and historical inferences concerning Beds I through IV in the Olduvai region.

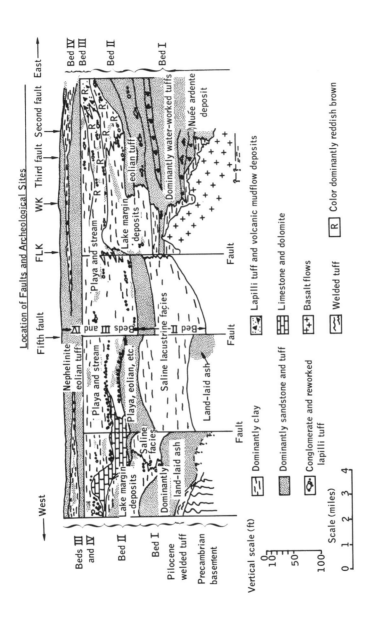

FIGURE 3. Stratigraphy of Beds I – IV along Olduvai Main Gorge, revised on the basis of work in 1964. Sequence is reconstructed using the base of the Eolian Tuff Member of Bed IV as a horizontal datum. Indicated fault displacements took place before the eolian tuffs of Bed IV were deposited. Subsequent faulting has displaced the eolian tuffs along these and other faults.

Bed I consists largely of trachyte pyroclastic deposits and flows of trachyandesite and basalt. Its thickness ranges from about 40 ft to more than 160 ft. In its easternmost exposures in the gorge, Bed I consists largely of water-worked trachyte tuffs, lapilli tuffs, and conglomerates. These deposits interfinger westward with tuffs and tuffaceous clays that were deposited in and near a shallow lake. Westward, beyond the lacustrine deposits, Bed I is mostly a weathered accumulation of land-laid trachyte ash. Eruptions of Ngorongoro supplied must of the trachyte ejecta in Bed I, as shown both by eastward coarsening of ejecta and by the orientation of stream channels filled with reworked ejecta.

The base of Bed II marks approximately the horizon at which a perennial saline lake became established; this lake existed in the axis of Olduvai Basin for most of the long period of deposition of Bed II (Figure 4). Unfossiliferous green clays form most of the saline-lacustrine sequence, and the remainder includes trachyte tuff,

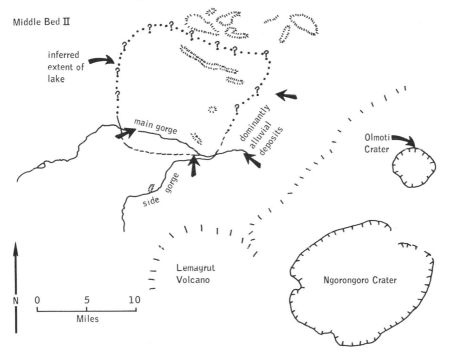

FIGURE 4. Paleogeography of the Olduvai Basin during deposition of Bed II prior to faulting in the basin. Arrows represent direction of stream transport as inferred from the orientation of stream channels and source directions of sedimentary detritus. The position of the shoreline in and near the gorge is inferred from lithology and fossils.

dolomite, limestone, and chert nodules. The lake lacked a permanent outlet, and during periods of heavy rainfall it expanded 2 to 3 miles east of its usual margin, flooding the marginal terrain with fresh or brackish water. At times the lake was probably chemically stratified, with fresh or brackish water overlying saline water in the axis of the basin. Fluvial deposits interfinger with lacustrine beds to the west, east, and south of the lake. Fluvial detritus to the west is of metamorphic origin; that to the south and east is volcanic. A zeolite-cemented deposit of wind-worked (eolian) nephelinite tuff is extensively developed at one horizon to the east of the lake (Figure 1). The easternmost exposures of Bed II above the eolian tuff consist largely of reddish-brown zeolite-bearing clays, sandstones, and tuffs.

Faulting destroyed the saline lake in the axis of the basin, and lacustrine clays that predated the faulting were succeeded by sandstones, clays, and conglomerates that were deposited in playa lakes, floodplains, and stream channels. Quartzose detritus, eroded from Precambrian rocks to the west and northwest, was transported progressively eastward and southward by streams during accumulation of the upper part of Bed II and all of Beds III and IV. Intermittently during formation of Beds III and IV, streams probably carried detritus to a developing fault graben east of the present-day Olduvai Gorge (Figure 5).

Beds III and IV have an aggregate thickness of 60 to 150 ft. These two units are clearly separated only in the eastern part of the gorge, where Bed III consists largely of analcimic reddish-brown volcanic conglomerates, sandstones, and claystones resembling the red beds in the upper part of Bed II. These reddish-brown volcanic clastic rocks of Bed III interfinger westward and northwestward with gray and brown clays and sandstones derived from the Precambrian basement rocks. Gray clays, sandstones, and conglomerates form most of the Lower Member of Bed IV, which includes a few zeolitic red beds in the eastern part of the gorge. Red beds of Beds II and IV can easily be mistaken for those of Bed III.

The upper layer, or Eolian Tuff Member, of Bed IV is 30 to 40 ft thick and consists largely of wind-worked nephelinite tuffs cemented by calcite and zeolites, with interbedded layers of calcrete (Hay, 1963b). Fragments eroded from the red bed facies of Bed III are present in conglomerates of the Eolian Tuff Member to the east of the Second Fault, indicating that erosion of the gorge had now begun.

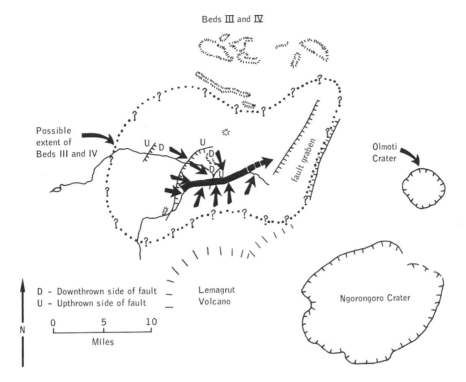

FIGURE 5. Paleogeography of the Olduvai Basin during deposition of
Beds III and IV. Arrows represent the direction of stream transport as
inferred from the orientation of stream channels and source directions
of detritus.

The distribution of hominid fossils and artifacts correlates with
the paleogeography inferred for the Olduvai region during accumulation of Beds I through IV. Within Bed I and the lower part of
Bed II, fossils and artifacts are concentrated along the inferred
southeastern edge of the lake, in the vicinity of streams draining
Ngorongoro and Lemagrut (Figure 4). Only one artifact site is
known from the west side of the saline lake of Bed II. In Beds III
and IV, artifacts occur chiefly in the vicinity of stream - channel
conglomerates derived from the west and northwest. Most of the
artifacts seem to be concentrated near the main east - west drain-
ageway (Figure 5). Few artifacts derived from Lemagrut have
been found in the deposits of Beds III and IV.

The climate of the Olduvai region through most of the Pleistocene time was probably relatively dry. Eolian tuffs of Beds II and

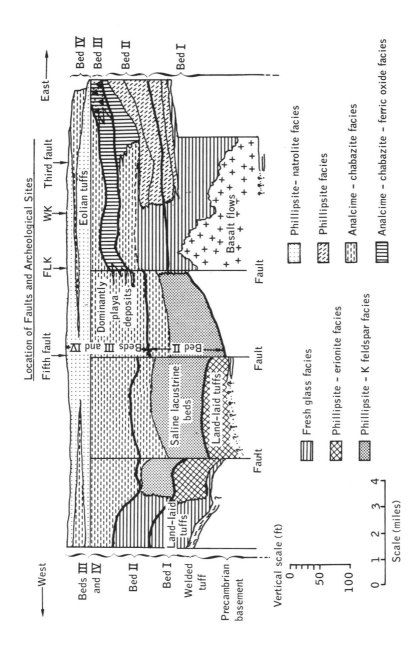

FIGURE 6. Stratigraphic diagram showing distribution of zeolitic mineral assemblages in Beds I – IV of Olduvai Gorge. Mineral distribution is based on field mapping and laboratory study by the writer.

IV accumulated in a desert or semidesert environment, much like
the present, in which vegetation was insufficient to prevent considerable reworking of volcanic ash by wind. Zeolitic alteration
of eolian tuffs and formation of calcrete are evidence of saline,
alkaline soils in which salts were concentrated at the land surface (Hay, 1963b; 1966). The saline lake of Bed II, represented
by the potassium feldspar - phillipsite facies of Figure 6, required a climate in which evaporation must have exceeded inflow
to the lake in most years. The writer has not observed saline
minerals or salt casts in these deposits, but beds of fine-grained
dolomite, abundant coarse euhedral crystals of calcite, and authigenic potassium feldspar, phillipsite, and searlesite in trachyte
tuffs suggest this water was rich in dissolved sodium carbonate -
bicarbonate and commonly attained salinities of 5 to 10 percent (Hay, 1964, p. 1,371). Salt casts are, however, both widespread and abundant 40 to 50 miles to the north of the Olduvai
Gorge in lacustrine deposits of the Peninj Beds (Figure 1) that
are at least partly correlative with Bed II (Isaac, 1965; Hay, 1966).
Land-laid trachyte tuffs of Bed I have been extensively altered
to phillipsite and erionite to a depth of 15 to 55 ft below the saline -
lacustrine facies of Bed II. This zeolitized part of Bed I constitutes the phillipsite - erionite facies, which mirrors perfectly the
overlying saline - lacustrine facies, suggesting that the zeolites of
Bed I were formed in contact with saline alkaline water of Bed II,
which moved downward and displaced the fresh water originally
present in the tuffs (Hay, 1966).

   Eolian tuffs of the phillipsite facies were zeolitized at the land
surface before burial, but zeolites of the phillipsite facies below
the eolian tuffs seem to reflect movement of saline, alkaline water
downward from the land surface. The base of the phillipsite facies
probably corresponds approximately to the water table at the time
the eolian tuffs were deposited and zeolitized. Beds between the
eolian tuffs and the water table may have been zeolitized by sodium-
carbonate solutions periodically flushed downward from the surface
during heavy rains.

   Clays of Beds III, IV, and the upper part of Bed II contain analcime, less commonly chabazite, and, rarely, phillipsite. Most of
the zeolitic clays are gray or brown (analcime - chabazite facies),
but some are bright reddish-brown (analcime - chabazite - ferric
oxide facies). The zeolites occur chiefly as fillings of narrow
shrinkage cracks and linings of root cavities. The highest concentrations of zeolites, about 20 percent of the sediment, are

found in resistant beds of reddish-brown and ocherous claystone. These zeolites apparently reflect chemical reactions of detrital silicate minerals with saline alkaline solutions concentrated in and near shallow, impermanent playa lakes.

Red beds of Beds II, III, and IV deserve special comment as they represent the chemical reactions of alluvium at the site of deposition in a dry climate, unlike many red beds of the geologic record, which are accumulations of sediment that was red before it was deposited. Much of the red color of the Olduvai red beds originated in oxidation of ferrous iron in pyroxene grains altering in a saline environment. The best modern analogy known to the writer is that of the delta of the Peninj River, on the west side of Lake Natron, a large shallow pond of sodium-carbonate - bicarbonate brine in the eastern Rift Valley approximately 50 miles to the northeast of Olduvai Gorge. Zeolitic red beds are in various stages of development on the low marginal part of the delta that is periodically flooded by saline, alkaline lake water (Hay, 1966).

The repeated episodes of zeolitic alteration in the Olduvai region probably reflect both the hot dry climate and an unusual abundance of sodium and carbonate ions. The entire eastern Rift Valley is extraordinarily rich in sodium carbonate, and dissolved sodium carbonate and bicarbonate characterized the majority of the present-day lakes and spring waters. Most of the sodium carbonate in the eastern Rift Valley may have originated in the weathering of sodium-rich volcanic rocks (Baker, 1958), but some of it has a direct volcanic origin. Flows of molten sodium carbonate were discharged from Oldoinyo Lengai in 1960, and sodium-carbonate ash was emitted in earlier eruptions (Dawson, 1962). Dawson has presented evidence for repeated carbonate-rich eruptions of late Pleistocene age from nephelinite volcanoes to the east and northeast of Olduvai Gorge. Prevailing winds are easterly and northeasterly and could easily have carried sodium-carbonate ash to the Olduvai region.

Three absolute-dating methods have been applied to Bed I, with substantial agreement on an age of nearly 2 million years for the lowermost hominid fossils and artifacts. In the extensive program of potassium - argon (K - Ar) dating by Evernden and Curtis (1965), one of the most secure dates is that of 1.70 to 1.75 million years for an ignimbrite that overlies the oldest artifacts and hominid remains. Marker Bed A, 25 to 30 ft above the ignimbrite, is 1.60 to 1.65 million years old, judging from K - Ar dates of this tuff and those immediately above and below it. Fission track dating of pumice in the ignimbrite has given an age of 2.03 ±0.28 million years (Fleischer et al., 1965), in substantial agreement with the K - Ar date. The lava flows of Bed I have normal magnetic polarity (Grommé and Hay, 1963) and give a K - Ar date of 1.9 million years (Evernden and Curtis, 1965). Only one short episode of normal polarity, having an age of 1.9 million years, has been recognized in the worldwide Matuyama epoch of reversed polarity spanning the interval from about 1 to 2.5 million years ago (Cox et al., 1964). Thus the polarity of the lavas of Bed I is appropriate to their K - Ar age of 1.9 million years, providing another example of agreement by two geophysical methods.

The dating program of Evernden and Curtis (1965) emphasizes the need for geologic information in evaluating the stratigraphic validity of isotopic dates. Basalt flows of Bed I, for example, gave an apparent age of 4.4 million years (Curtis and Evernden, 1962), yet the relatively fresh pahoehoe surface on the basalts suggested that they were extruded and buried only a relatively short time before discharge of the ignimbrite, giving a date of 1.70 to 1.75 million years (Hay, 1963a). Redating the basalts by an improved procedure gave an age of 1.9 million years (Evernden and Curtis, 1965). Another example, biotite, giving an age of 1.0 to 1.1 million years, was at the time of collection thought to represent Bed I but was subsequently assigned to Bed II on mineralogic grounds (Hay, 1963a). Later a detailed investigation of the site strongly suggested that the dated sample had been taken from Bed V, which unconformably overlies Bed II at this point (Hay, 1965). Evernden and Curtis (1965) found that most if not all samples of visibly reworked or contaminated tuff of Bed I yield ages too old to be accepted as valid, thus indicating that petrographic information can be useful in assessing the validity of K - Ar dates. A small amount of contaminating detritus may be difficult to detect, and a series of dates on samples from known stratigraphic levels is clearly the most effective way to detect errors in isotopic dating, as Curtis and Evernden have amply demonstrated for Beds I and II.

ACKNOWLEDGMENTS

Dr. and Mrs. L. S. B. Leakey provided camp facilities and assisted my work in many ways. I also wish to acknowledge the cooperation of my colleagues G. H. Curtis and J. F. Evernden. Financial support was provided by the Miller Institute for Basic Research in Science (Berkeley), the National Geographic Society, and the Associates of Tropical Biogeography at the University of California at Berkeley.

42

REFERENCES CITED

Baker, B. H., 1958, "Geology of the Magadi Area," Geol. Surv. Kenya Rept., 42, 81.

Cox, A., R. R. Doell, and G. B. Dalrymple, 1964, "Reversals of the Earth's Magnetic Field," Science, 144, 1,537-1,543.

Curtis, G. H., and J. F. Evernden, 1962, "Age of Basalt Underlying Bed I, Olduvai," Nature, 194, 610-612.

Dawson, J. B., 1962, "The Geology of Oldoinyo Lengai," Bull. Volcanol., 24, 349-387.

Evernden, J. F., and G. H. Curtis, 1965, "The Potassium-Argon Dating of Late Cenozoic Rocks in East Africa and Italy," Current Anthropol., 6, 343-383.

Fleischer, R. L., P. B. Price, R. M. Walker, and L. S. B. Leakey, 1965, "Fission-Track Dating of Bed I, Olduvai Gorge," Science, 148, 72-74.

Grommé, S., and R. L. Hay, 1963, "Magnetization of Basalt of Bed I, Olduvai Gorge, Tanganyika," Nature, 200, 560-561.

Hay, R. L., 1963a, "Stratigraphy of Beds I through IV, Olduvai Gorge, Tanganyika," Science, 139, 829-833.

Hay, R. L., 1963b, "Zeolitic Weathering in Olduvai Gorge, Tanganyika," Geol. Soc. Am. Bull., 74, 1,281-1,286.

Hay, R. L., 1964, "Phillipsite of Saline Lakes and Soils," Am. Mineralogist, 49, 1,366-1,387.

Hay, R. L., 1965, "Comments on "The Potassium-Argon Dating of Late Cenozoic Rocks in East Africa and Italy," G. H. Curtis and J. F. Evernden, Current Anthropol., 6, 367.

Hay, R. L., 1966, "Zeolites and Zeolitic Reactions in Sedimentary Rocks," Geol. Soc. Am., Spec. Paper 85, 130.

Isaac, G. L., 1965, "The Stratigraphy of the Peninj Beds and the Provenance of the Natron Australopithecine Mandible," Quaternaria, 7, 103-130.

Leakey, L. S. B., 1951, Olduvai Gorge, Cambridge University Press, New York, 163 pp.

Leakey, L. S. B., 1965, Olduvai Gorge, 1951-61, Vol. 1, A Preliminary Report on the Geology and Fauna, Cambridge University Press, New York, 118 pp.

Leakey, L. S. B., and M. D. Leakey, 1964, "Recent Discoveries of Fossil Hominids in Tanganyika: at Olduvai and near Lake Natron," Nature, 202, 5-7.

Pickering, R., "A Contribution to the Geology of the Olduvai Gorge," Geol. Survey of Tanzania, Report RP/23 (in press).

Reck, H., 1951, "A Preliminary Survey of the Tectonics and Stratigraphy of Olduvai," pp. 5-19 in Olduvai Gorge, L. S. B. Leakey, Cambridge University Press, New York, 163 pp.

Absolute Dating
and the History of Man

WILLIAM T. PECORA and MEYER RUBIN
U.S. Geological Survey

TWO separate concepts of time have plagued geologists since the beginning of their science some 200 years ago. One is relative, or "systemic," and the other is chronometric, or "absolute." Discovery of radioactivity by Becquerel in 1896 and subsequent efforts by Rutherford, Boltwood, and Nier started a chain of scientific efforts that is proving to be successful in welding the two concepts into a useful and interchangeable time scale of geologic events.

Sequence dating has been the foundation of the systemic time scale. As implied by Poincaré (1913, p. 223), the recognition of singular events in sequence makes up an important part of man's concept of time. Applied to geologic investigations, this intellectual process involves an understanding of succession as well as concurrency of events. Woodford (1963) has assigned first order importance to sedimentary succession in a single region and poses as the major problem the necessity of establishing validity in concurrency, or correlation, in tying one region to another. The sciences of geology and archeology became mature while only this time concept was in use; and although communication was excellent among geologists or among archeologists, because of internal consistency of their systemic time scales, their time jargon was unintelligible to mathematicians, physicists, and chemists.

The concept of chronometry was proposed by Synge (Whitrow, 1961, p. vii) primarily to demonstrate time (chronometry) and space (geometry) as equally important elements of the universe. The "celestial clocks" of Price (1961, p. 23) were evidence of the ability of man to understand the chronometric units provided by observations of his solar system. Chronometry, then, offered the mechanism to measure the duration of geologic events or of earth history in terms universally understandable.

Holmes (1913, p. 10) has recounted the controversy between Lord Kelvin, the physicist, and his contemporary geologists in the period 1850 to 1900. By an empirical method and elegant mathematics, Lord Kelvin calculated the age of a cooling earth to be between 20 and 100 million years—a figure not at all acceptable to geologists. One geologic method after another failed to destroy the rigorous methodology of physics; and although geologists were vocal in their disbelief of so short an age span, their view was based on the depth of their understanding of geologic processes rather than on rigorous scientific expression. It was the recognition of radioactivity that invalidated Kelvin's primary assumption and hence his problem solution. In time, however, the principle of rhythmic layering as proposed by Gilbert in 1895 and later applied by Geer (1912), Bradley (1929), and others might have been a mechanism to integrate geologic events and chronometry; but radioactive systems—and again physics—provide the most promising keys to the rigorous time solution.

Geochronometry has now reached an advanced state of craftsmanship. However, it is so often shrouded in mystic symbols that the technique per se is frequently misnamed geochronology. Our crying need for absolute dating of geologic events or materials has spurred such massive efforts by geophysicists during the past two decades that the activity along the path has raised, on the one hand, a host of geologic believers whose hope and faith are so frenetic that they have become uncritical, and, on the other, a host of geologic doubters who refuse to accept the probability that many gems lie within the handful of "number" grains offered them.

The purpose of this review is to evaluate the numbers and methods applicable to geologic events of the past few million years, particularly with reference to man or to hominid remains. Because geologic techniques of correlation are so insensitive to stratigraphic sections formed under continental conditions, absolute dating will very likely be the most rewarding technique if we can but apply some rigid validity controls.

Validity, or integrity, must be fulfilled in each of three areas: (1) experimental method employed, (2) geochemical "fitness" of the sample, and (3) geologic intelligence. Ideally, then, we can get "right" answers that can stand the test of most critical scrutiny. Experience has shown that if a group of knowledgeable geologists unanimously accepts an age assignment of a rock or mineral the chances are very good that the date is essentially correct. By the same token, if serious doubts are raised, all three "validities" need re-examination. The experimental and geologic validities are more amenable to successful re-examination, however, than geochemical validity of the samples. The experimentalists have been using the mass approach in their attempts toward greater geochemical validity. All applicable dating methods and all possible materials are being used. This shotgun approach is not thoroughly satisfacory but is recognized as part of the evolution of the science. The possibility that all methods used today are wrong must be acknowledged.

EXPERIMENTAL VALIDITY

Experimental work dealing with dating has been in the mainstream of research for two decades and has been characterized by an environment of invention. Validity is a function of the limitations imposed by the equipment used or devised; of the uncertainty of the physical constants, chemical analyses, and spectrographic apparatus; and of the firmness of the very assumptions of the method itself.

The dating methods we are concerned with as applicable to the last few million years of the geologic time scale include carbon-14 dating, potassium - argon (K - Ar) dating, and a whole group that can be called the uranium-series methods. Broecker (1965) has reviewed the several methods pertinent to the Pleistocene (see Table 1). In addition, there are the fission-track and obsidian dating methods, which are of a different genre. Isotopic ratios as a guide to temperature of carbonate formation are pertinent to our review.

All radiogenic dating methods operate on the hourglass mechanism. They depend on the principle of a measurable amount of parent material decaying at a fixed rate to a measurable amount of daughter products in a supposedly closed system. This means that there can be no addition or loss of parent or daughter product by means other than the ticking of this clock during the

TABLE 1. Summary of Pleistocene Age-Dating Methods[a]

Isotope	Half-life (10^3 yr)	Method	Range (10^3 yr)	Materials	Likelihood of Applicability to[b]				
					Ocean Temperature	Sea Level	Glacier Extent	Arid Lakes	Pollen Sequence
^{14}C	5.7	Decay	0–35	Organics – calcium carbonate	+	+	+	+	+
			35–70	Organics					
^{231}Pa	32.0	Decay	5–120	Red clay	+				
		Integration	5–120	or					
		^{230}Th normal	5–120	Globigerina ooze		0	0	0	0
^{230}Th	75.0	Decay	5–400	Red clay	+				
		Integration	5–400	or					
		^{230}Th normal	5–400	Globigerina ooze		0	0	+	+
		Growth	0–200	Organics – calcium carbonate	0	+	0	+	
^{234}U	250.0	Decay	50–1,000	Coral	0	+	0	0	0
^{4}He	—	Growth	no limit	Mollusks or coral	0	+	0	+	0
^{40}Ar	—	Growth	no limit	Volcanics	+	+	+	+	+
^{36}Cl	300.0	Growth	50–500	Igneous or metamorphic rock	0	0	+	0	0
^{10}Be	2,500.0	Decay	100–8,000	Red clay	+	0	0	0	0

a After Broecker, 1965.
b + signifies applicable; 0 signifies not applicable.

time range under review. Geologists would never grant that such a closed system exists in the crust of the earth, although there is much less opportunity for these additions or losses to take place in the relatively short time of Pleistocene and Recent.

An interesting problem has developed in ^{14}C dating, casting doubt on the basic assumption that activity of ^{14}C has been in the same equilibrium state in the atmosphere throughout its applicable dating range (but preatomic bomb). By measuring ^{14}C activity of Sequoia tree rings, daters found that atmospheric concentration has oscillated, with an average amplitude of 3 percent, from the present concentration during the past few thousand years (Figure 1). Measurements on the older bristlecone pine, however, indicate a rising concentration curve, so that for a date of 5,000 years a correction of 600 years is necessary. What is the extrapolation of this trend? We may yet find that the radiocarbon time scale is a rubber-band scale that can be stretched or contracted with each glaciation and interglaciation.

Currently, the half-life constant used for ^{14}C is 5,568 years. Although general agreement exists that 5,730 (recently established) is a better figure, the older one continues to be used. All published data, however, state what constants are employed.

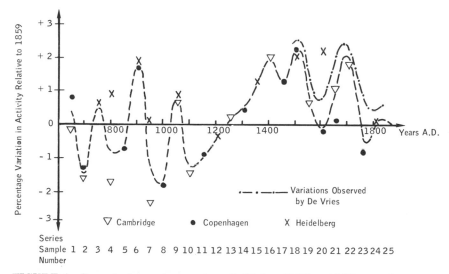

FIGURE 1. Sequoia tree ring series. Initial activities of 25 samples taken at 50-year intervals from a giant sequoia, represented as a percentage variation from the activity of the wood from the 1859 tree ring. (After Willis et al., 1960.)

Experimental precision in mass spectrometry has improved so notably that even with a half-life of 1.3 billion years in K - Ar decay, reproducibility of the measurement of ^{40}A is commonplace. This is evidence of the great progress achieved over two decades in instrumentation and precision of laboratory procedures. But because the initial assumptions of the methods themselves are less firm, reproducible results demonstrate merely the precision of the technique and not full validity of the numbers.

GEOCHEMICAL VALIDITY

Geochemical integrity permits determination of which minerals or rocks are indeed best for which methods. Leakage, alteration, inclusions, contamination, or recrystallization may cause rocks and minerals to tell false stories. Too frequently, different minerals in the same sample yield different ages by the same or other methods.

Some years ago, bone material, shells, and vegetative matter were all believed to be acceptable for ^{14}C dating. Today, bone material is used with considerable reservation, and shell dates are not considered reliable beyond 30,000 years, and even within that range they may have a possible error of 2,000 years.

In samples for K - Ar dating, we suspect that inherited argon exists in fluid inclusions in many minerals. Rama et al. (1965), for example, demonstrated this to be true for inclusions in quartz. Currently, one investigator is measuring several modern flows to see if they are dated as zero age, as they should be. The recognition of inherited argon recently caused correction of the age estimate for the Bishop Tuff by Dalrymple et al. (1965) from 1.0 to 0.7 million years. Minerals and rocks undergoing hydrothermal or surficial alteration do not provide a closed system for retention of all the potassium and argon or for withstanding invasions from other sources.

The assumptions regarding initial conditions are in even more serious difficulties in the uranium-series methods. Those depending on known thorium and uranium concentrations are plagued by detrital phases of sediments, whereas authigenic growth is usually assumed. With the ^{10}Be method, the concentration of this isotope is so small that it is difficult to determine just how much the ocean sediment should have contained initially. Experimenters using most of these methods have suffered the

embarrassment of trying to explain nonzero ages at the very
top of the sediment core.

Contamination by atmospheric ingredients is particularly
acute in young volcanic glass that has undergone surficial alteration. Leaching outer layers of rock or mineral samples with
hydrofluoric acid helps in removing possible atmospheric argon
contamination. Earlier, ^{14}C daters removed the humic acid
fraction from wood samples by boiling them in alkali and from
surface layers of carbonate samples by treatment with HCl. Un-
recognized natural contamination can prove to be serious in
young age samples. For example, a rock or mineral granular
sample from East Africa containing one Precambrian grain per
thousand (0.1 percent) can recast a zero age as 2 million years.

Geochemical validity of a sample is almost impossible to predict. Careful petrologic and mineralogic evaluation is necessary
before beginning experimental procedure. The present search
is directed toward minerals that do not normally exchange or
absorb and that contain large quantities of the isotope in question.
Whole rock samples, once in disrepute, are now often considered
choice samples for dating. Hornblende, once ignored, is now
being used. For the K - Ar method, certainly samples rich in
potassium are necessary. The tide has turned, in some circles,
against the use of glauconites. But the fitness of samples frequently is determined after much fumbling.

GEOLOGIC VALIDITY

If experimental precision is the least suspect and geochemical
validity the least determinable, then certainly geologic validity
is the most controversial. To develop a universal Pleistocene
time scale we must correlate marine sediments of the Mediterra-
nean with those of the ocean deeps and continental shelves, with
ash falls in Africa, lava flows in Iceland, river terraces and
cave deposits in Europe, continental glacial deposits and moun-
tain glaciers in North America, and coral in the Atlantic. The
task is herculean. These are the materials being dated today,
and their interpretation is critical to the construction of a
Pleistocene time scale.

But when did the Pleistocene begin? The Pliocene - Pleistocene boundary as now accepted is based on faunal changes in
the Calabrian type section of Italy. Historically, the Pleistocene

time scale was determined by the depth of leaching on glacial
soils, using the time since the last glaciation as the yardstick.
This unit of time was estimated by extrapolating from the rate
of waterfall retreat in a few critical places. When the estimated
time span was reduced by ^{14}C dating from 25,000 to 11,000 years,
the estimate of the duration of the entire Pleistocene was corres-
pondingly reduced from 1 million years to 500,000 years. The
oxygen isotope work of Emiliani (1955) appeared to substantiate
the short scale.

The most important impact of K - Ar dating in recent years is
reestablishment of the longer chronometry. Evidence to support
this reversal is mounting. Some dates on continental deposits
have stretched the Pleistocene to a duration of 2 or even 3.5
million years, if the deposits in question are truly Pleistocene as
claimed. The ^{14}C dating of the fluctuations of the surface ocean
temperature as reflected in the $^{18}O/^{16}O$ ratio of the carbonates
in foraminifera in deep-sea cores has proved to be an important
breakthrough. Emiliani (1955) plotted oscillations of his isotopic
data as valid variations in ocean temperature and therefore implied valid correlation with planetary glacial episodes (Figure 2).
The ^{14}C ages of the sediments assigned dating from the present
to just short of the last interglacial, however, and the extrapolation beyond was based on interpretation of the peaks in temperature variation. Protactinium - ionium dates (Rosholt et al., 1961)
substantiated part of this extrapolation. According to Emiliani's
phases, the beginning of the four continental glaciations occurred
some 300,000 years ago, and the Pleistocene began 600,000 years
ago. His interpretation places strong reliance on complete geologic validity in the continuous record of the cores, the correlation
of continental glaciation and oceanic temperatures, the rate of
sedimentary accumulation, and the absence of significant temperature fluctuations within each of the glacial stages.

Emiliani (this volume, p. 56) recognizes the difficulties in the
geologic method, saying, "... it is difficult or impossible to correlate the oceanic and continental stratigraphies, as well as different continental stratigraphies, except by absolute dating." He
is correct in reserving correlations until the marine stage of the
Calabrian has been dated. His current temperature curve carries
no continental correlations (Emiliani, 1966).

A different time scale, also using the evidence from deep-sea
cores, was arrived at by Ericson et al. (1964). Morphological
changes in foraminiferal assemblages permitted a different

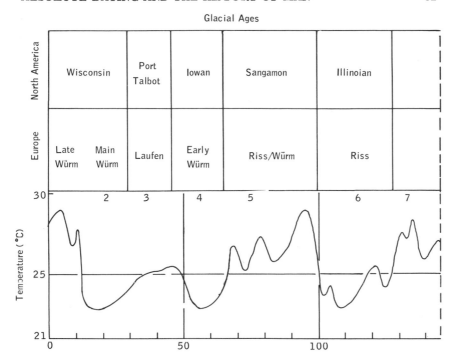

Glacial Ages

FIGURE 2. Generalized temperature curve and absolute time scale (by extrapolation for dates beyond 150,000 years B.P.). Modified from Rosholt et al., 1961.)

interpretation of the importance of fluctuations (Figure 3). Ericson placed the beginning of the Pleistocene at 1.5 million years. Unfortunately K - Ar dating is not applicable to deep-sea cores. Emiliani questions the validity of the Ericson correlations on several grounds (Emiliani, 1964), pointing to internal contradictions in the method. If continental glaciation can be correlated with deep-sea cores, certainly the Emiliani and Ericson positions, each based initially on valid techniques, need re-examination and resolution.

If not by sea, then perhaps by land, correlation can be accomplished. In California, the Bishop Tuff, overlying a till of Kansan(?) age (Blackwelder, 1931), was dated by Dalrymple et al. (1965) as 0.7 million years. In Iceland, a till contained in a section of basalt flows is dated as about 3.1 million years. The Villafranchian fauna of France, considered by some to be Pleistocene in age, has been dated by an associated tuff deposit

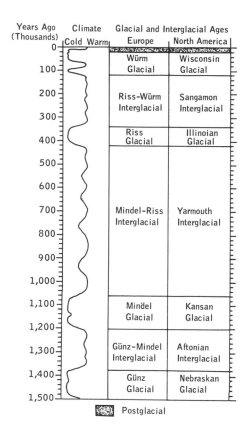

FIGURE 3. Pleistocene time scale and generalized climate curve based on the study of deep-sea sediment cores. The beginning of the Pleistocene is considered to be the onset of the first glaciation, the Nebraskan or Günz. (After Erickson et al., 1964.)

at more than 3 million years. In contrast to these dates, however, the Upper Main Terrace of the Rhine, correlated with the Günz or first, glaciation, has been dated at 400,000 years. This underscores the priniple that, where the geologic evidence is fallible, the results of dating are not valid even if the dating methods are.

The paleomagnetic - polarity technique developed by Cox et al. (1965) is emerging as an aid to correlation. It depends on observations that the earth's magnetic field changes with time and that certain rocks are permanently magnetized in the earth's field at the time of their formation. Lava flows measured for their polarity and their K - Ar dates lend themselves to a kind of magnetic time scale. Once there is agreement on the placement of the Pliocene - Pleistocene boundary in the polarity epoch time scale, the normal or reversed polarity of the rocks can be used as a correlation technique (Figure 4).

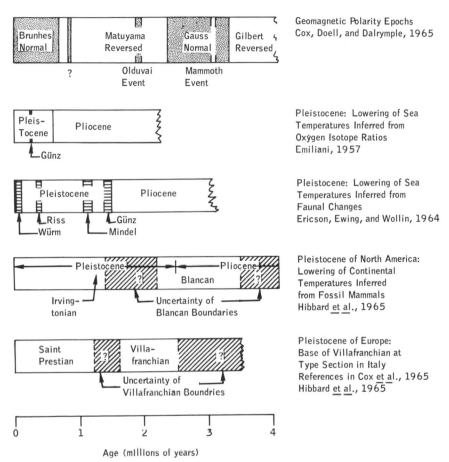

FIGURE 4. Geomagnetic polarity time scale, and various time scales for the Pleistocene. (Courtesy of Allan Cox and Richard Doell, in press.)

CASE HISTORY OF OLDUVAI

The combination of methods used in the investigations at Olduvai Gorge—absolute dating, sampling, and stratigraphic correlation—provides a good example of the kind of investigative approach needed for most localities before any confidence can be placed in the chronometry of geologic events. Straus and Hunt (1962) most properly called attention to the conflicts implied in the first dates published by Leakey et al. (1961) and cautioned against acceptance of any of the dates until much further work is done in the field and in the laboratory. Subsequent geologic study by Hay (1963) clarified some of the complex problems of correlation, provided a better basis for selection of samples, and afforded Everden and Curtis more opportunity to test their experimental procedures to obtain higher confidence in their results. A second field visit by Hay (this volume, p. 30), coupled with a detailed laboratory examination of mineral samples, increased the geologic intelligence of the site. A date of 1.8 million years for the part of Bed I containing Zinjan-thropus is the most acceptable and apparently was the best of the three dates that formed the target of the Straus-Hunt review. Fleischer et al. (1965) obtained a fission-track age of 2.03 ± 0.28 million years on a pumice from Bed I. Despite the apparent agreement, the question of who collected the pumice, and with what geologic controls and validity, should be emphasized. The incorrect use of "bed" in Bed I and Bed II will unfortunately remain in the literature concerning the site.

CONCLUSIONS

It has become increasingly evident that under ideal conditions ^{14}C dating can exceed 30,000 years and K-Ar dating can extend its lower range to meet it, thus covering the entire Pleistocene time scale. The two scales may not be interchangeable, however, although many people would like them to be. The probability of ideality and truly "absolute" chronometry is too remote to be expected, except perhaps for an odd sample. For the most part, we may expect groups of samples to be acceptable or valid only after serious review, re-examination, and evaluation in a relative sense of proportion. Geochronometry in this light can then be derived through geochronology. Intercontinental correlation and chronometry during the hominid span remain an open question, still subject to a great deal of speculative interpretation. Absolute dating methods, however, still offer the most promising means of achieving this aim if the concept of full validity is not lightly put aside.

REFERENCES CITED

Blackwelder, E., 1931, "Pleistocene Glaciation in the Sierra Nevada and Basin Ranges," Geol. Soc. Am. Bull., 42, pp. 865-992.

Bradley, W. H., 1929, "The Varves and Climate of the Green River Epoch," U.S. Geol. Survey Prof. Paper 158, 87-110.

Broecker, W.S., 1965, "Isotope Geochemistry and the Pleistocene Climatic Record," in The Quaternary of the United States, H. E. Wright, Jr., and D. G. Frey, eds., Princeton University Press, Princeton, N.J., 922 pp.

Cox, A., and R. R. Doell, "Paleomagnetism and Quaternary Correlation," INQUA Symposium VII, Boulder, Colo., August 1965 (in press).

Cox, A., R. R. Doell, and G. B. Dalrymple, 1965, "Quaternary Paleomagnetic Stratigraphy," pp. 817-830, in The Quaternary of the United States, H. E. Wright, Jr., and D. G. Frey, eds., Princeton University Press, Princeton, N.J., 922 pp.

Dalrymple, G. B., A. Cox, and R. R. Doell, 1965, "Potassium-Argon Age and Paleomagnetism of the Bishop Tuff, California," Geol. Soc. Am. Bull., 76, 665-674.

Emiliani, C., 1955, "Pleistocene Temperatures," J. Geol., 63, 538-578.

Emiliani, C., 1964, "Paleotemperature Analysis of the Carribean Cores A254-BR-C and CP-28," Geol. Soc. Am. Bull., 75, 129-144.

Emiliani, C., 1966, "Paleotemperature Analysis of Carribean Cores P6304-8 and P6304-9, and a Generalized Temperature Curve for the Past 425,000 Years," J. Geol., 74, 109-126.

Ericson, D. B., M. Ewing, and G. Wollin, 1964, "The Pleistocene Epoch in Deep-Sea Sediments," Science, 146, 723-732.

Fleischer, R. L., P. B. Price, R. M. Walker, and L. S. B. Leakey, 1965, "Fission Track Dating of Bed I, Olduvai Gorge," Science, 148, 72-74.

Geer, G. de, 1912, "A Geochronology of the Last 12,000 Years," Congr. Geol. Int., Stockholm, 1910, pp. 241-253.

Hay, R. L., 1963, "Stratigraphy of Beds I through IV, Olduvai Gorge, Tanganyika," Science, 139, 829-833.

Hibbard, C. W., 1965, "Quaternary Mammals of North America," in The Quarternary of the United States, H. E. Wright, Jr., and D. G. Frey, eds., pp. 509-525, Princeton University Press, Princeton, N.J., 922 pp.

Holmes, A., 1913, The Age of the Earth, Harper Brothers, London, 196 pp.

Leakey, L. S. B., G. H. Curtis, and J. F. Evernden, 1961, "Age of Bed I, Olduvai Gorge, Tanganyika," Nature, 191, 478.

Poincaré, H., 1913, The Foundations of Science, Science Press, New York, 553 pp.

Price, D. J. de S., 1961, Science Since Babylon, Yale University Press, New Haven, Conn., 149 pp.

Rama, S. N. I., S. R. Hart, and E. Roedder, 1965, "Excess Radiogenic Argon in Fluid Inclusions," J. Geophys. Res., 70, 509-511.

Rosholt, J. N., C. Emiliani, J. Geiss, F. F. Koczy, and P. J. Wangersky, 1961, "Absolute Dating of Deep-Sea Cores by the Pa-231/Th-230 Method," J. Geol., 69, 162-185.

Straus, W. L., and C. B. Hunt, 1962, "Age of Zinjanthropus," Science, 136, 293-295.

Whitrow, G. J., 1961, The Natural Philosophy of Time, Thomas Nelson and Sons Ltd., London, 324 pp.

Willis, E. H., H. Tauber, and K. O. Munnich, 1960, "Variations in the Atmospheric Radiocarbon Concentration over the Past 1,300 Years," Am. J. Sci., Radiocarbon Suppl., 2, 1-4.

Woodford, A. O., 1963, "Correlation by Fossils," in The Fabric of Geology, C. C. Albritton, ed., Addison-Wesley Publishing Company (for Geological Society of America), Reading, Mass., pp. 75-111.

DISCUSSION

Stratigraphic Correlations and the Pleistocene Epoch

CESARE EMILIANI
Institute of Marine Science
University of Miami

CLASSICALLY, sedimentary deposits are correlated by means of their characteristic fossils. However, the time elapsed since the late Pliocene, amounting to less than a few million years, is too short for appreciable speciation among invertebrates to have occurred. As for land vertebrates, while speciation proceeded with unusual speed because of the rapidly and drastically changing environmental conditions, these very changes, by blocking and rerouting animal migrations, create uncertainties as to the synchronism of the occurrence of the same species in distant locations.

The discovery that four (Penck and Brückner, 1909) or five (Calvin, 1897) glaciations occurred during the Pleistocene has led to the almost universal usage of Pleistocene climatic change and its geologic effects as a means of stratigraphic correlation. As an example, the ferretto of Lombardy is inferred to correlate with the Mindel-Riss interglacial of the northern slope of the Alps because of its leaching and oxidation, and younger and older deposits are identified with respect to this datum. Using the same technique, together with some carbon-14 control, the author proposed a tentative correlation between oceanic temperature stages and the accepted continental stratigraphy of Europe and North America (Emiliani, 1955).

Subsequent research (Emiliani, 1966a, 1966b) has confirmed what was in effect already suggested by Arrhenius's analysis of eastern equatorial Pacific cores (Arrhenius, 1952), namely, that there are more than four or five Pleistocene stages. Thus, nine warm stages and eight cold stages were found to have occurred during the past 425,000 years (Emiliani, 1966a, Figure 6). In addition, significant temperature oscillations were detected in deposits as old as late Pliocene (Emiliani et al., 1961), leading to the inference that some 20 temperature cycles per million years may have occurred during the past one or two million years. This high frequency seems to have escaped the attention of most paleontologists and paleobotanists, apparently because of insufficient sampling or because of incorrect ecologic assumptions. On the one hand, the coarse sampling generally imposed by the distribution of macrofossils in marine epicontinental deposits has made it difficult for macropaleontologists to recognize the fine alternations of warmer and colder conditions and has led to assigning "cool" conditions to the entire thickness of Calabrian and Sicilian deposits (see Ruggieri, 1961, references). On the other hand, sampling of the same deposits at much closer stratigraphic intervals, made possible by the abundance and distribution of microfossils (foraminifera), has easily led to the detection of the alternations mentioned above not only by $^{18}O/^{16}O$ analysis but also by purely micropaleontological methods (Emiliani et al., 1961, 1962).

Accurate micropaleontological study of deep-sea cores and computer analysis of the data has yielded paleoclimatic curves that are practically identical with those obtained by the $^{18}O/^{16}O$ method (Lidz, 1966). These curves differ from those published by Ericson and Wollin (1956a, 1956b), Ewing et al. (1958), and Ericson et al. (1961) only because the paleoecological assumption upon which the latter are based (namely, that the relative abundance of the Globorotalia menardii group is directly proportional to temperature) is incorrect. In fact, important core sections in which the Globorotalia menardii group is rare or absent (and therefore classified as cold by the authors mentioned) contain in great abundance species that are far more restricted to warm water

TABLE 1. Ages of Continental and Oceanic Stages[a]

Continental Stages			Oceanic Stages		
Name	Age (Year B.P.)	Method of Dating	No.	Age (Yr B.P.)	Method of Dating
Late Wisconsin	10,000–25,000	^{14}C	2	10,000–25,000	^{14}C
Middle Wisconsin (Port Talbot – Plum Point, Worozonfian)	25,000–55,000	^{14}C	3	25,000–50,000	^{14}C
Early Wisconsin	55,000–70,000	^{14}C	4	50,000–67,000	^{14}C (Extrap.)
Pelukian	100,000	$^{230}Th/^{238}U$	5	96,500[b]	$^{231}Pa/^{230}Th$
Kotzebuan	172,500	$^{230}Th/^{238}U$	7	171,500[b]	$^{231}Pa/^{230}Th$
Middletonian	217,500	$^{230}Th/^{238}U$	9	218,000[b]	$^{231}Pa/^{230}Th$

[a]Data from Rubin and Suess, 1955, 1956; Rosholt et al., 1961, 1962; Blanchard, 1963; Goldthwait et al., 1965; Emiliani, 1966.
[b]Temperature maxima.

than the Globorotalia menardii group (cf. Emiliani, 1964). In view
of the detailed criticism brought against the methods employed
by the authors in question, it is both surprising and disappointing
that some writers (e.g., Pecora and Rubin, this volume, p. 43)
should still assign validity to the paleoclimatic reconstructions
of Ericson, Ewing, and associates, and should still consider the
resulting variance between these reconstructions and those published by the present writer an unresolved problem.

With the single exception of the oceanic stage 3 (equivalent to
the Port Talbot - Plum Point interval), the amplitude of the oceanic
temperature oscillation did not vary much during the past 425,000
years. The quasi constancy in wavelength and amplitude of these
oscillations, as evidenced by both $^{18}O/^{16}O$ and micropaleontological analysis, suggests that the distinction between stadials and
interstadials (in the European sense) may have to be re-examined.
The distinction, in fact, cannot be made in the oceanic sections.
In this context, it is suggestive that the total number of the recognized Günz and post-Günzian stadials and interstadials (nine cold
and nine warm: see Flint, 1957, p. 386) is approximately the same
as that predicted by the oceanic temperature curve if the age of
about 400,000 years determined for the first stage of the Günz
by $^{40}K/^{40}Ar$ dating (Frechen and Lippolt, 1965) is accepted.

Because of the increased number of major temperature oscillations now known to have occurred during the Pleistocene, it is
difficult or impossible to correlate the oceanic and continental
stratigraphies, as well as different continental stratigraphies,
except by absolute dating. In addition, because of the high frequency of the Pleistocene temperature oscillations, it is not possible to correlate any two given continental stages in different
sections unless they are both dated by absolute methods with an
analytical and field error smaller than one half the wavelength of
the oscillations (or less than 20,000 years). Few of the dates thus
far published for material older than about 60,000 years seem to
meet this requirement (cf. Pecora and Rubin, this volume, p. 43).
Among the dates are the $^{230}Th/^{238}U$ determined by Blanchard
(1963) for the interglacial Alaskan deposits named Worozonfian,
Pelukian, Kotzebuan, and Middletonian. These deposits appear to
correlate with, respectively, the oceanic stages 3,5,7, and 9. In
addition, the continental stages late, middle, and early Wisconsin
are known, by ^{14}C dating, to correlate with the oceanic stages
2,3, and 4. These correlations are so close (Table 1) as to leave
little doubt that subsequent absolute age measurements on various

continental deposits will result in identifying the deposits as belonging to one or another of the numerous oceanic temperature oscillations.

The problem of the age of the Pliocene - Pleistocene boundary, defined as the time of the first appearance in abundance of the benthonic foraminiferal species Hyalinea (Anomalina) baltica (Schroeter) in the section at Le Castella, Calabria, southern Italy (VIIth INQUA Congress, Denver, 1965), remains unsolved.* However, volcanic ash occurring in the section at Le Castella may provide suitable material for absolute dating. Until such dating is achieved, the age of the boundary can only be estimated very roughly. Also, it is not possible to gauge the classic Villafranchian - Calabrian correlation. The current trend is to regard much of the Villafranchian as Pliocene.

If the Pliocene - Pleistocene boundary is defined in a way different from the classic one, then the age of the boundary is likely to be different. Thus, if the boundary is placed at the beginning of the Günz glaciation, the age appears to be about 400 thousand years (Frechen and Lippolt, 1965); if it is placed at the time of the first appearance of the Villafranchian fauna, an age somewhat greater than 3.3 million years is expected (Curtis, 1965; Obradovich, 1965). Failure of scholars to define their Pleistocene and of reviewers to understand these difficulties has lead to innumerable semantic impasses. With the unanimous restatement by the VIIth INQUA Congress of an exact definition of the Pliocene - Pleistocene boundary, which is in effect very close to or identical with the original one for the base of the Calabrian (Gignoux, 1913), there should be no more discussion of a "long" Pleistocene chronology as opposed to a "short" one. In fact, the estimated duration of the Pleistocene has not changed since Gignoux defined the Calabrian in 1913 and since the Calabrian was assigned to the Pleistocene (XVIIIth International Geological Congress, London, 1948). What has changed is the age of the Günz glaciation, which was formerly estimated at about 600 thousand to 1 million years (cf. Zeuner, 1945; Flint, 1957); later estimated at about 300 thousand years (Emiliani, 1955); now measured at about 400 thousand years (Frechen

*Ericson et al. (1964) claim to have reconstructed an entire Pleistocene section by patching en échelon a number of deep-sea cores from the Atlantic and the Caribbean. However, the almost entire lack of correlation between the cores below the top row in their Figure 3 and the incorrect assumption upon which their temperature reconstructions are based combine to make altogether meaningless the generalized climatic curve and Pleistocene correlations presented by these authors.

and Lippolt, 1965). Also changed is the age of the beginning of the Villafranchian, formerly estimated at 600 thousand to 1 million years and now measured at somewhat more than 3.3 million years. However, the formal definition of Pleistocene does not rest upon the Günz or the Villafranchian but upon the beginning of the marine stage Calabrian, an event whose age remains unknown to the present time.

REFERENCES CITED

Arrhenius, G., 1952, "Sediment Cores from the East Pacific," Swedish Deep-Sea Expedition, 1947-1948, Rept., 5, 1-227.

Blanchard, R. L., 1963, "Uranium Decay Series Disequilibrium in Age Determination of Marine Calcium Carbonates," Ph.D. thesis, Department of Chemistry, Washington University, St. Louis, Mo.

Calvin, S., 1897, "Synopsis of the Drift Deposits of Iowa," Am. Geol., 19, 270-272.

Curtis, G., 1965, "Potassium-Argon Date for the Early Villafranchian of France," Trans. Am. Geophys. Union, 46, 178 (abs.)

Emiliani, C., 1955, "Pleistocene Temperatures," J. Geol., 63, 538-578.

Emiliani, C., 1964, "Paleotemperature Analysis of the Caribbean Cores A254-BR-C and CP-28," Geol. Soc. Am. Bull., 75, 129-144.

Emiliani, C., 1966a, "Paleotemperature Analysis of Caribbean Cores P6304-8 and P6304-9, and a Generalized Temperature Curve for the Past 425,000 Years," J. Geol., 74, 109-126.

Emiliani, C., 1966b, "Isotopic Paleotemperatures," Science, 154, 851.

Emiliani, C., A. Gianotti, and T. Mayeda, 1962, "Analisi Isotopica dei Foraminiferi Siciliani delle Argille di Ficarazzi, Palermo," Quaternaria, 5, 135-141.

Emiliani, C., T. Mayeda, and R. Selli, 1961, "Paleotemperature Analysis of the Plio-Pleistocene Section at Le Castella, Calabria, Southern Italy," Geol. Soc. Am. Bull., 72, 679-688.

Ericson, D. B., and G. Wollin, 1956a, "Correlation of Six Cores From the Equatorial Atlantic and Caribbean," Deep-Sea Res., 3, 104-125.

Ericson, D. B., and G. Wollin, 1956b, "Micropaleontological and Isotopic Determinations of Pleistocene Climates," Micropaleontology, 2, 257-270.

Ericson, D. B., M. Ewing, and G. Wollin, 1964, "The Pleistocene Epoch in Deep-Sea Sediments," Science, 146, 723-732.

Ericson, D. B., M. Ewing, G. Wollin, and B. C. Heezen, 1961, "Atlantic Deep-Sea Sediment Cores," Geol. Soc. Am. Bull., 72, 193-286.

Ewing, M., D. B. Ericson, and B. C. Heezen, 1958, "Sediments and Topography of the Gulf of Mexico," in Habitat of Oil, L. Weeks, ed., American Association of Petroleum Geologists, pp. 995-1,053.

Flint, R. F., 1957, "Glacial and Pleistocene Geology," John Wiley & Sons, Inc., New York, 553 pp.

Frechen, J., and H. J. Lippolt, 1965, "Kalium-Argon-Daten zum Alter des Laacher Vulkanismus, der Rheinterrassen und der Eiszeiten," Eiszeitalter Gegenwart, 16, 5-30.

Gignoux, M., 1913, "Les formations Marines Pliocenes et Quaternaires de l'Italie du Sud et de la Sicile," Université Lyon, Annales, n.s., I, 36, 693 pp.

Goldthwait, R. P., A. Dreimanis, J. L. Forsyth, P. F. Karrow, and G. W. White, 1965, "Pleistocene Deposits of the Erie Lobe, in The Quaternary of the United States, H. E. Wright, Jr., and D. G. Frey, eds., pp. 85-97, Princeton University Press, Princeton, N.J., 922 pp.

Lidz, L., 1966, "Deep-Sea Pleistocene Biostratigraphy," Science, 154, 1,448.

Obradovich, J. D., 1965, "Isotopic Ages Related to Pleistocene Events," VII INQUA Congress, Boulder, Colorado (abs.).

Penck, A., and E. Brückner, 1909, "Die Alpen im Eiszeitalter," Tauchnitz, Leipzig, 1,199 pp.

Rosholt, J. N., C. Emiliani, J. Geiss, F. F. Koczy, and P. J. Wangersky, 1961, "Absolute Dating of Deep-Sea Cores by the Pa^{231}/Th^{230} Method," J. Geol., 69, 162-185.

Rosholt, J. N., C. Emiliani, J. Geiss, F. F. Koczy, and P. J. Wangersky, 1962, "Pa^{231}/Th^{230} Dating and O^{18}/O^{16} Temperature Analysis of Core A254-BR-C," J. Geophys. Res., 67, 2,907-2,911.

Rubin, M., and H. E. Suess, 1955, "U.S. Geological Survey Radiocarbon Dates II," Science, 121, 481-488.

Rubin, M., and H. E. Suess, 1956, "U.S. Geological Survey Radiocarbon Dates, III," Science, 123, 442-448.

Ruggieri, G., 1961, "Alcune Zone Biostratigrafiche del Pliocene e del Pleistocene Italiano," Riv. Ital. Paleont. Strat., 67, 405-417.

Zeuner, F. E., 1945, "The Pleistocene Period," Ray Soc., London, 322 pp.

DISCUSSION

Application of Fission Track Dating to Anthropology

ROBERT L. FLEISCHER
General Electric Research and Development Center

SPONTANEOUS fission of ^{238}U impurities provides a tool for absolute dating in many materials of geologic and anthropologic interest, by creating natural radiation-damage tracks. These tracks may be identified optically by means of chemical etching; their number increases with the uranium content and the age of the sample. A count of new tracks induced by neutron irradiation in a reactor allows the uranium content to be found and the age to be computed from the natural track density. This method has been described extensively in the literature (see References Cited), including four review articles (Fleischer, Price, and Walker, 1964b; 1965a; 1965d; 1965e), one of which is specifically concerned with anthropological applications (Fleischer, Price, and Walker, 1965a) such as the dating of the Olduvai Bed I pumice (Fleischer, Price, Walker, and Leakey, 1965a). The details of track identification (Price and Walker, 1963; Fleischer and Price, 1964a; 1964b; 1964c; Brill et al., 1964; Fleischer, Price, and Walker, 1964a) and stability (Fleischer and Price, 1964b; 1964c; Fleischer, Price, and Walker, 1965b; 1965d), of usable materials (Fleischer, Price, and Walker, 1965d; Fleischer and Price, 1964c; Fleischer, Naeser, Price, Walker, and Marvan, 1965), and of uranium content needed for dating samples of a given age (Fleischer, Price, and Walker, 1965a; Fleischer and Price, 1964c) have been documented in existing literature; they will not be repeated here.

It is enough to note that (1) one part per million by weight of uranium will allow an age as low as 100,000 years to be measured without undue difficulty and an age of 10,000 years with considerable labor (Fleischer, Price, Walker, and Leakey, 1965b); (2) each mineral type must be assessed for its track-retaining properties (Fleischer and Price, 1964b; 1964c; Fleischer, Price, and Walker, 1965b; 1965d); and (3) any crystals that are used must have a diameter of at least a track length $(\approx 8\text{-}12\,\mu)$. The problem of selecting a material has two major factors: to find datable samples and to find samples whose age can be proved to be relevant to the fossil of interest. Neither by itself is difficult, but solving the two parts of the problem simultaneously is usually not easy to do.

REFERENCES CITED

Brill, R. H., R. L. Fleischer, P. B. Price, and R. M. Walker, 1964, "The Fission Track Dating of Manmade Glasses: Part I, Preliminary Results," Glass Studies, 6, 151.

Fleischer, R. L., and P. B. Price, 1964a, "Fission Track Evidence for the Simultaneous Origin of Tektites and Other Natural Glasses," Geochim. Cosmochim. Acta, 28, 755.

Fleischer, R. L., and P. B. Price, 1964b, "Glass Dating by Fission Fragment Tracks," J. Geophys. Res., 69, 331.

Fleischer, R. L., and P. B. Price, 1964c, "Techniques for Geological Dating of Minerals by Chemical Etching of Fission Fragment Tracks," Geochim. Cosmochim. Acta, 28, 1,705.

Fleischer, R. L., P. B. Price, and R. M. Walker, 1964a, "Fission Track Ages of Zircons," J. Geophys. Res., 69, 4,885.

Fleischer, R. L., P. B. Price, and R. M. Walker, 1964b, "Fossil Records of Nuclear Fission," New Scientist, 21, 406.

Fleischer, R. L., P. B. Price, and R. M. Walker, 1965a, "Applications of Fission Tracks and Fission Track Dating to Anthropology," 7th International Congress on Glass, Brussels, June - July 1965, Proceedings, E. Plumat and R. Chambon, eds. (also available as G.E. Res. Lab. Report 65-RL-3878M).

Fleischer, R. L., P. B. Price, and R. M. Walker, 1965b, "Effects of Time, Temperature, and Ionization on the Formation and Stability of Fission Tracks in Minerals and Glasses," J. Geophys. Res., 70, 1,497.

Fleischer, R. L., P. B. Price, and R. M. Walker, 1965c, "On the Simultaneous Origin of Tektites and Other Natural Glasses," Geochim. Cosmochim. Acta, 29, 161.

Fleischer, R. L., P. B. Price, and R. M. Walker, 1965d, "Solid State Track Detectors: Applications to Nuclear Science and Geophysics," Ann. Rev. Nucl. Sci., 15, 1-28.

Fleischer, R. L., P. B. Price, and R. M. Walker, 1965e, "Tracks of Charged Particles in Solids," Science, 149, 383.

Fleischer, R. L., P. B. Price, E. M. Symes, and D. S. Miller, 1964, "Fission Track Ages and Track-Annealing Behavior of Some Micas," Science, 143, 349-351.

Fleischer, R. L., P. B. Price, R. M. Walker, and L. S. B. Leakey, 1965a, "Fission Track Dating of Bed I, Olduvai Gorge," Science, 148, 72-74.

Fleischer, R. L., P. B. Price, R. M. Walker, and L. S. B. Leakey, 1965b, "Fission Track Dating of Mesolithic Knife," Nature, 205, 1,138.

Fleischer, R. L., C. W. Naeser, P. B. Price, R. M. Walker, and U. B. Marvin, 1965, "Fossil Charged Particle Tracks and Uranium Distributions in the Minerals of the Vaca Muerta Meteorite," Science, 148, 629.

Maurette, M., P. Pellas, and R. M. Walker, 1964, "Étude des Traces de Fission Fossile dans le Mica," Bull. Soc. Franc. Mineral. Crist., 87, 6.

Price, P. B., and R. M. Walker, 1963, "Fossil Tracks of Charged Particles in Mica and the Age of Minerals," J. Geophys. Res., 68, 4,847.

Man and Novelty

LOREN C. EISELEY

University of Pennsylvania

"THE SKULL as the shell of the brain," the linguist Max Müller (1891) once remarked, "has been supposed to betray something of the spiritual essence of man." From the time of the first evolutionists and even before, in the writings of those entranced by the subtle organic transitions represented in the scale-of-nature philosophy, it was the human cranium that occupied the attention of the comparative anatomist. Even in the emptiness of death it represented man, for, in life, it was from the soundless dark domain of the cerebral hemispheres that there emerged the very language that symbolized, defined, and eternally reconstituted our cultural world. One distinguished modern paleontologist, D. M. S. Watson (1928), has confessed that "those structures whose qualities can alone explain the meaning of man's evolution lie beyond his sight." To persist, therefore, in the attempt to assess the time involved in the rise of the human brain is to involve oneself, not alone with man, but with his works. One of man's first, most efficacious tools has left, unfortunately, no direct traces in the earth. Language, whose constituents have come down the long traverse of millennia as rolled and pounded by circumstance as a flint ax churned in a river bed, leaves no direct traces of its dim beginnings. Its creations, moreover, are frequently confused with the innate capacities of the brain that gave them birth.

65

The brain of man is a device unlike any other on the planet, a device for the production of novelty, for drawing more from nature than meets the self-contained eye of a sunning lizard or a bird. The role of the brain is analogous in a distant way to the action of mutation in generating improbabilities in the organic realm. Moreover, the human brain appears to be a remarkably solitary product of this same organic process which, in actuality, it has transcended. In this sense life has produced, after the passage of some three billion years, a newly emergent instrument capable of transmitting a greatly speeded-up social heredity, based not upon the gene but instead upon communication. In its present technological phase it has brought the ends of the world into conflict and at the same time is reaching outward into space.

Man's future is even more obscure than his beginnings. To venture to sound either depth is to enter an unknown, perhaps unknowable, realm, but it is a characteristic of man that he constantly attempts these journeys. If we do so here in an effort to examine the past from which we have so recently emerged, it is with no expectation of solving the precise way in which a ground-dwelling biped became the most extraordinary creature in the universe open to our observation. Rather it is because we seek to examine the complex of problems that the paleontology and archaeology of such a being presents to us, problems in some degree unique and thus not totally comparable to our studies of the evolution of other forms of life.

About man there always lingers a penumbral rainbow—what A. L. Kroeber termed the superorganic—that cloud of ideas, visions, institutions which hover about, indeed constitute human society, but which can be dissected from no single brain. This rainbow, which exists in all heads and dies with none, is the essential part of man. Through it he becomes what we call human, and not otherwise. Thus he is, as John Donne recognized three centuries ago, "a part of the continent, a piece of the Main." Man is not totally contained in a solitary skull vault nor measurable as, say, a saber-toothed cat or a bison is measurable. Something, the rainbow dancing before his eyes, the word uttered by the cave fire at evening, eludes us and runs onward. It is gone when we come with our spades upon the cold ashes of the campfire 400,000 years removed. And the skull, too, confronts us with a faint grin, keeping its essential secret through a hundred measurements.

So many human fragments have now been discovered that it is easy to grow overconfident in our assessment of present knowledge and to assume much for which we have as yet little empirical evidence. Our fossils are scattered over the widest areas of the Old World land mass—in some instances drawn from lands whose geology is very inadequately known. Some remains lie outside the swing of the continental glaciations and can only be dated by the use of known fossils. The glaciations themselves are constantly being reassessed as to time and number. Some scholars would contract the Pleistocene epoch, others would extend it. Some devoted students would see in the sequences of a single area the entire story of human evolution; others survey the world and multiply side branches on the tree of man. As James Beerbower (1960, p. 187) has remarked of the African problem alone, "The morphologic studies have been careful and ingenious but their significance to the interpretation of human evolution is clouded by inadequate stratigraphic background."

In spite of the growing number of human fossils, therefore, it is possible to recognize that while the major insights proposed by the Darwinians of the nineteenth century have been buttressed, their theoretical explanations of human evolution have proved less tenable. Darwin and his colleagues saw clearly that man was descended from some earlier small-brained primate, but the peculiar nature of the human animal forced even Darwin to have recourse to the concept of inherited habit. Wallace, on the other hand, saw further into what would prove to be the anthropological problems of the twentieth century. In seeking an explanation, however, he relapsed into a fatal mysticism, while Darwin's hesitations and ambiguities escaped notice.

Wallace proposed two major stages in the history of man after the latter's descent from an arboreal existence. He visualized a small-brained, upright phase in which man had perfected his bipedal adaptation to the vertical posture before his face and brain began to alter toward the form they now bear. Today that phase is clearly indicated by such discoveries as the various australopithecines and Homo habilis, if we wish to give this creature another name.

The second phase of human evolution Wallace regarded as the most important in the history of man, and I believe no one would dissent from his view today. Obviously, he could not fix the point at which the protohuman brain became human. He saw clearly, however, what the more biologically oriented Darwin had missed: that with the appearance of symbolic thought and speech, the old particulate evolution adapted to specific environments was, in the case of man, largely outmoded. Man would now rapidly project upon his created tools and machines what would previously have demanded millennially slow biological adaptation. Modification of organic parts would be transcended by the selection of ideas in the brain. Wallace did not mean that minor physiological adjustments and variations would cease in man. He merely regarded the human body as essentially approaching, if it had not already attained, its final shape. One would have to pierce very far into the past, he contended, to find man's body so altered as to show particulate evolution still shaping the human form.

It is suggestive, as revealing Wallace's perceptive intuition, to quote the following from Washburn and Howell's remarks of 1960 (p. 45):

> As technical efficiency increases, the structural diversity among hominids at any given time level decreases. Among those at the australopithecine stage, at least three distinct groups are known from the present geographically restricted material.... It is especially interesting that Homo sapiens, although inhabiting a far wider area and very diverse ecological zones, shows only racial differences.

Wallace had reasoned out, in other words, what the human paleontologist was to reveal empirically only after the passage of a century.

Since these observations make clear that man's primary specialization, the brain, along with the encephalized tongue and hand, have created an entirely unique situation in the realm of nature known to us, it is obvious that our efforts to understand the rise of this remarkable organ are made difficult by its singularity. Paradoxically, the purpose of the human brain is to escape physical specialization by the projections of thought. There is no parallel organism with which to compare ourselves. The creature from which we arose has perished. There is no twilight world of living fossils on the direct hominid line which we can subject to examination. At best we are forced to make inferences from less closely related primates whose activities lie below the threshold of speech. The nineteenth century, in the efforts of men like Hughlings Jackson, came to see the brain as an organ whose primary parts had been laid down successively in evolutionary time, a little like the fossil strata in the earth itself. The centers of conscious thought, like the clear ice of the Pleistocene epoch, were the last superficial deposit on the surface of a more ancient and irrational world. As the roots of our phylogenetic tree pierce deep into earth's past, so our human consciousness is similarly

embedded in, and in part constructed of, pathways which were laid
down before man in his present form existed. To acknowledge
this fact was still to comprehend as little of the brain's true
secrets as an individual might understand of the dawning of his
own consciousness from a single egg cell.

Nor is it possible to consider the brain without reference to
the vessels that feed it. The relatively huge organ demands oxygen out of all proportion to the rest of the body. We pay a high
metabolic price for supreme consciousness. The arterial system
to supply it had to evolve with the brain. Moreover, so large a
brain demands special arrangements for birth and postnatal care.
This, in turn, demands a familial structure sufficient to afford
protection, over an extended period, to a helpless larval offspring.
The number of such correlated features that have been, and are
now, necessary for human survival is quite astonishing. We know
nothing of the gene complexes involved or the mode of their origin.
We know, in fact, nothing about the number of genes controlling
brain size. The growth of that organ has been rapid, as far as the
geology of the past can inform us, but whether the ascent has been
steady or in explosive spurts is less evident because the direct
phylogenetic line is unclear. Australopithecine ground dwellers
of doubtful tool-using capacity persist into the middle Pleistocene.
In other areas paleanthropic, if not near neanthropic, forms of
true men are simultaneously in evidence.

If these datings are even approximate, we are faced with the
proposition that bipedalism alone does not insure cranial expansion. It is possible to postulate different ecological niches and
devise a set of habits that retard one group while another achieves
further advances toward a truly human status. It may be so, but
we should not blind ourselves to the fact that there is a touch of
Kipling's animal fables about our guesswork. The explanations
are ingenious but long on imagination. They should never lull
us with the notion that we have genuinely solved the problem
until our evidence is far more complete.

The appearance of a symbol-using brain, which opened the
doorway to a radically new corridor of existence, has been justi-
fiably hailed as a quantum step in evolution. By either the long
or short time scale of the Pleistocene, it may be termed an explosive event. If some type of rapid orthoselection is responsible
for that brain, one must seek for the nature of that selection as
well as the preadaptations that promoted its emergence. Since
orthogenetic evolution of a teleological character has fallen into

disfavor, the tendency in modern paleontology has been to seek for those adaptive innovations which at first glance appear conservative but which prove accidentally to be the key to a locked doorway into a new environmental world. The walking fins and the lung sac of the Devonian Crossopterygian fishes were such an accident. These organs having promoted survival in drying, unoxygenated stream beds, the creatures finally wandered away from their unsatisfactory water haunts. Other instances, such as the origin of the cleidotic egg, have been cited by Romer. Biological inventions of this kind have been most generally called preadaptations. Hockett and Ascher (1964, p. 72), labeling the principle "Romer's rule," have expressed it succinctly as follows:

> The initial survival value of a favorable innovation is conservative, in that it renders possible the maintenance of a traditional way of life in the face of changed circumstances.

Few would deny that the protohominids had been subjected to altered circumstances, but the two-phase nature of the change forces us to ask whether a set of preadaptations permitting movement from the trees to the ground initiated the entire sequence of events leading to modern man, or whether some additional later factor promoted the final cranial expansion not shared, apparently, by all of the near-men.

We can best begin this analysis by turning to the first prehuman phase, a phase which, in actuality, incorporates elements from the arboreal world itself; these preadaptations, derived originally from the Old World forest attic, involve the particulate organic evolution of the natural world. Combined in one order of life, however, an order which still contains living representatives besides modern man, we can glimpse in a far-off, shadowy fashion the creature from whom we sprang. It is like looking at the composite picture of a missing person created from the descriptions of many witnesses. We will learn much, but not all. The visage will seem to grow clearer, or recede, as under rippling water, yet in essence it adumbrates even in its dim beginnings the face of our father man.

Before turning to the opening of the cultural corridor which has enabled man to pass into a previously unimaginable domain of existence, it is worth relisting certain of those bodily predispositions that play a role in human development, even though one must draw qualifying lines by remarking that not all primates possessing these characters have become men. First, we may

note that the climbing propensities of the higher primates have
promoted neurological adjustment to the upright posture. The
verticality of their habitat zone has promoted in the activities of
most primates a similar (at least partial) verticality of adjustment
that was later to encourage, in the hominid line, the maintenance
of a bipedal stance upon the ground. Along with this departure
from the ground, the eye of the advanced primates has overridden
the old smell-brain of the more ancient forms of life. A creature
whose world is not stable, and through which he must hurtle on
the waving arms of trees, does not alone develop locomotor adaptability; that adaptability must be equally coordinated with the eye.

Such a stereoscopic three-dimensional scanning organ has, of
course, an unseen analogue in the brain. The visual areas must
increasingly judge, and judge with survival accuracy, depths and
heights, chasms and textures. Do the leaves ahead conceal a
branch capable of bearing the weight of one's body ? In the in-
stant of leaping or swinging the brain must know, as it must also
know simultaneously a possible life-saving alternative of movement. All life is adventure, but the tree world, for a nonflying
creature, is increasingly a world of futures ordered by a world
of past experience. The proprioceptive senses must be acute, and
agility of action must be matched by agility of mind. Foresight
must literally run ahead of sight and be guided by the feedback of
memory. Even today our common speech expresses time in the
language of space.

As for the hand, that organ is forced to move constantly through
an arboreal laboratory of leaves, waving branches, tree boles,
and tropical vine cables. The forest is an elementary tool shop.
Hands grasp, curl, release, and manipulate in a diversity of movement unknown to the average ground dweller whose limbs are
specialized for locomotion. Too long an apprenticeship in an attic
workshop may, it is true, produce a brachiating forelimb, which
in its turn follows the old particulate path of specialization. The
human forerunner escaped that cul-de-sac, but he brought with
him to the ground a forelimb selected and fitted for conscious,
deliberate control, just as he brought also the enriched accompanying mind of a gregarious animal.

It is at least conceivable—and the possibility has been broached
in the case of the porpoise—that an advanced brain and strong
communal instincts can emerge in another medium. The remarkable aspect of the human adventure lies in the fact that one general-

ized operational tool, the freed hand and forelimb, was placed in the service of the brain. The porpoise, by contrast, however intelligent he may prove to be, has been forever denied one of the two necessities for the creation of the true superorganic: the ability actually to manipulate substance.

In summary, we may say that the preadaptations which, in a latent sense, had opened the doorway to life upon the ground lay in the bodily adaptations we have just discussed, themselves the product of the tree world and, in addition, the fact that the human ancestor, like all the higher primates, was a social animal. We may safely infer from living examples that some group concern for the protection of females and the young was manifest at all times. Moreover, the arboreal world is one in which call signals of location, danger, warning, and a small variety of other necessary sounds help to transmit information among creatures frequently in dense foliage and invisible to one another.

It is not necessary to label such signals as speech. They deal with immediate necessities, not with the past or the abstract. Nevertheless, it would be foolish to ignore that in minds of sharpened perception and even limited memory these sounds convey feeling states, or that reaction to them is heightened by experience and observation. A thin and very misty layer of truly "learned," if preconditioned, response hovers about such signals. The sound "stands for"—it is not the visible thing. Nevertheless, it is not speech, and it is still very largely an act of instinct— that is, an inherited expression and response which is yet capable of some degree of softening or heightening as anxiety or feeling tone dictates. It is here that memory and experience may begin to play a modifying role.

If we now turn to Wallace's first phase of the truly human adventure, the bipedal intrusion upon the ground, we are confronted by anatomical alterations which must have involved an enormous stretch of time and for which the 10 million years or so of Pliocene time give us but fragmentary and inadequate glimpses. As F. Clark Howell (1959, p. 840) and others have observed, this transformation involved "a basic reorientation of the pelvis in relation to the trunk, interrelated changes which permitted an erect trunk and full extension of the lower limbs in stable, upright posture (and, in the female, maintenance of the bony birth canal)." Such changes included a considerable shifting of muscles, alteration of the pelvis, secondary adaptation of the foot to walking instead of climbing, and associated modifications of the femur and knee joint.

There is no possible way at present of determining the length of this transition, its selective intensity, or what induced it, beyond the obvious fact that a grass or savannah corridor must have been open to exploitation. Our knowledge of human genetics is not adequate to determine the number of actual gene changes involved. Once man had been fully established as a ground dweller, however, it is obvious that natural selection, building upon an already existing genotype, would have been diverted into quite a different direction. It is at this level that the most primitive-shaped tools make their appearance, and to many thinkers traditional stone working clearly marks archeologically the emergence of true speech. Since the African savannah is thought by many to be the original homeland of humanity, and since man's descent to the ground was perhaps one of the most biologically traumatic of his many adventures, it is well to reassess at this point the significance of preadaptation and the dynamism implicit on life itself, and to what extent these latter two conceptions coincide or are unconsciously opposed to each other in human thinking.

Ours is a mechanically inclined and man-centered age. Not many months ago, I was perusing a work on space when I came across this statement by a professional astronomer: "Other stars, other planets, other life, and other races of men are evolving all along, so that the net effect is changeless" (Page, 1962, p. 18). Implied in this remark was an utter confidence that the evolutionary process was everywhere the same, ran through the same succession of forms, and emerged always with men at the helm of life, men presumably so close to ourselves that they might interbreed—a supposition fostered by our comic strips.

In the light of this naive orthogenesis—for such it is—let us consider just two worlds we know about, not worlds in space, but continents on our own planet. These continents exist under the same sun and are surrounded by the same waters as our own; their life bears a distant relationship to ours but has long been isolated. Man never arose in the remote regions of South America and Australia. He only reached them by migration from outside. They are laboratories of agelong evolution which tell us much about the unique quality of the human experience.

The southern continents of our earth do not maintain the intimacy of faunal exchange that marks the land masses of Holarctica encircling the basin of the polar sea. Instead, they are lost in the southern latitudes of the oceans and for long intervals their faunas have evolved in isolation. These lands have been in truth "other worlds."

The most isolated of these worlds is Australia. With the insignificant exception of a few late drifters from outside, this marsupial world—for such it is—is not merely an ancient world. It is a world in which ground life, originally represented by a few marsupial forms, has, since the Mesozoic, evolved untroubled by invading placental mammals from without. Every possible ecological niche from forest tree to that of underground burrower has been occupied by the evolutionary radiation of a slower-brained mammal whose young are born in a far more embryonic condition than that of the true Placentalia. This world remained unknown to western science until the great exploratory voyages began. Somewhere in the past, life had taken another turn. Chance mutation, "total contingency" in Gregory's words, had led to another stochastic model. The "world" of Australia contained no primates at all, nor any hint of their emergence. Upon that "planet" lost in the great waters, they were one of an infinite number of random potentialities which had remained as unrealized as the whole group of placental mammals, of which the Primate order is a minor part.

If we now turn to South America, we encounter still another isolated evolutionary center—but one not totally unrelated to that of Eurasia. Here, so the biogeographers inform us, an attenuated land bridge, at intervals completely severed, has both stimulated local evolutionary development and at times interrupted it by migrations from North America. Our concern is with just one group of animals, the South American monkeys. They are anatomically distinct from the Catarrhine forms of the Old World, and constitute an apparent parallel emergence from the prosimians of the early Tertiary. Once more, however, even though the same basic Primate stock is involved, things have gone differently. There are no great apes in the New World, no evidence of ground-dwelling experiments of any kind. Though fewer carnivores are to be found on the South American grasslands than in Africa, the rain-forest monkeys, effectively equipped with prehensile tails, still cling to their archaic pathways. One can only observe that South America's vast rivers flow through frequently flooded lowlands, and that by contrast much of Africa is high, with open savannah and parkland. The South American primates appear confined to areas where descent to the ground proved less inviting. Here ended another experiment which did not lead to man, even though it originated within the same order from which he sprang. Another world had gone astray from the human direction.

If, as astronomers occasionally extrapolate, man was so ubiquitous, so easy to produce, why had two great continental laboratories, Australia and South America—"worlds," indeed—failed to reproduce him? They had failed, we may assume, simply because the great movements of life are irreversible, the same mutations do not occur, circumstances differ in infinite particulars, opportunities fail to be grasped, and so what once happened is no more. The random element is always present, but it is selected on the basis of what has preceded its appearance.

There exists also a living screen of successfully adapted life which may either stifle a new experiment in its beginning or permit the newcomer to slip through and become, through further selection, sufficiently adapted to hold his own. These openings may be infrequent.

The creature that was to become man sprang through such a doorway before it was sealed behind him. His ancient cousins watch him now from behind the diminishing trees. The door has closed.

I speak of man as "springing" through such an opening, but what in reality did he do, and how long did it take him? It is at this point that we must fully grasp what is meant by preadaptation in a purely mechanical sense. It must be linked to that endless experimentation that is part of the restless curiosity of life and that reaches its most intense expression in mammals. It is occasionally suggested that man became a ground dweller and erect because he was forced out of the trees by drought and continental uplift; that he was, in short, the hapless, hopeless victim of circumstance. When his origins were regarded as Asian, this view used to be expressed in connection with the Himalayan uplift; today, in other versions involving Africa, the same views are expressed, along with the supposition that the human ancestor was driven out into the grasslands by larger and more formidable foraging relatives. None of these views demands outright rejection, but I should like to introduce a cautionary note of dissent.

We have seen by our little venture into continental biology that there appears nothing foreordained about the human emergence, or any orthogenetic trend demanding man's constant reappearance either on this planet or elsewhere. In spite of popular confusion, I believe a knowledge of evolutionary principles defeats the theory of even random duplication. To fall back upon preadaptation is certainly advisable, but I do not believe that an active experimental primate, such as we may assume the human ancestor to have been, needs necessarily to have been thrust from his home in nature by one convulsive act, as is frequently implied, even if not intended, in some of these discussions.

We have seen that the attainment of an arched walking foot and a remodeled body suggests changes that must have taken place by incremental alterations in the structure of a much slighter creature than modern man. Even beginning with preadaptations toward an upright body stance—a thing that can be observed among some of the existing lemurs—it would appear that the necessary time to perfect these adaptations does not suggest any sudden departure from the normal routines of life. Rather, if we recognize the nature of the African savannah, its parkland, its swarming fauna which suggests a long rich period of development, it is not difficult to imagine that proto-man may have begun his career by experimental ventures out into the parkland or along its fringes while selection slowly whittled his body into the outlines it bears today.

Life is a constant matter of experimental centrifugal pressure outward against its environment. During the course of my life I have encountered a squirrel on a subway platform, pigeons on my bookcases, and a flying squirrel who had set up housekeeping in the drawer of a kitchen cabinet. Their acts were totally exploratory. Newspapers are spotted with such anecdotes. They stretch back through time. They involve a teetering, half-human creature who was on the point of wielding objects in a way no creature had done before. Perhaps, after the passage of more millennia than we care to visualize, the creature walked away forever from his last refuge in a clump of trees. By then a stick may have dangled in his hands, but I suspect nothing would have driven him from his cluster of trees if by then the grass had not had the familiar appearance of home. With seeds and grasshoppers, wild sorghums, and small mammals he would now be fed. He was catholic in his tastes. Even today we know that what might truly be called cultural innovation may make one Primate group such as the baboons accept flesh which another might reject.

The tool-using activities of Homo habilis and other australopithecines have long been under discussion. Western society is highly tool-conscious, and it is my personal belief that altogether too much weight has been given to the tool as the creator of the human brain. After all, the latent resources of the human intellect are tremendous. Technology in the complicated sense we know is largely the product of the last three centuries, yet men

totally outside the western tradition have mastered it. The motor
area for the thumb and forefinger are well represented in the
cortex, but equally so is the tongue, with the accompanying fine
auditory discrimination.

I do not question that the invention of tools has added to the
complexities, even indirectly, that the brain has had to master.
It is merely my contention that speech formation and reception
has demanded far more involved anatomical preparation and
selection—selection that had to run across an entire group more
or less simultaneously in order to have value. We have noted
the preadaptations promoting it, but even so it is the most remarkable evolutionary step on the planet, a true quantum achievement that has literally given man, in some degree, the creative
powers of nature.

The transition from instinctive sign to formally transmitted
symbol has left no traces, nor need it be equated with the first
recognizable artifact of a stoneworking tradition. As Hockett
and Ascher (1964, p. 84) have pertinently observed, "Speaking
of things which are out of sight or in the past or future is very
much like carrying a weapon when there is no immediate use for
it. Each of these habits thus enforces the other." The social
arrangements of a simple band unit might well have demanded
incipient speech forms long before an identifiably shaped object
was left on a cave floor. One need only walk along the gravel
bed of a river to see what useful stones can be picked up and
used without the knowledge necessary to shape them. In fact,
the first working of flint may have come about as the by-product
of observing accidental fractures in the use of just such stones.

The animal, by and large, seeks to satisfy his immediate
hunger and his reproductive instincts. Man, as his vocabulary
and memory extend, becomes apperceptive rather than plain
perceptive. He envisages what is out of sight, or an hour off, or
a year away. His sentiments extend beyond himself to his group.
As Hallowell has so ably pointed out in a number of papers, the
concept of self emerges. The "I" can think of "me." It is here,
in intimate association with language, that the quantum step is
glimpsed. The self assumes roles in the societal web, it ingests
not just food but values. Hallowell (1959, p. 59) comments:

> The great novelty then, in the behavioral evolution of the primates,
> was not simply the development of a cultural mode of adaptation as such.
> It was, rather, the psychological restructuralization that not only made
> this new mode of existence possible but provided the psychological basis

for cultural readaptation and change. The psychological basis of culture lies not only in a capacity for highly complex forms of learning but in a capacity for transcending what is learned; a potentiality for innovation, creativity, reorganization and change.

In a passage earlier in this paper we quoted Washburn and Howell on the steady reduction and elimination of marked human distinctions as one ascends the time scale. We pointed out that, in the mind of Alfred Russel Wallace, this was the inevitable climax of the human achievement—the escape from specialization except in brain. Throughout the Pleistocene, vast orogenies—the advance and retreat of continental glaciations—must have sharpened the cutting effects of selection upon man. Lagging and archaic bipeds vanished from the scene, and there is still a marked unconformity between the first known appearance of sapiens and his true source in time. Moreover, if we pass backward to the second interglacial, we encounter in Swanscombe man a modern brain, irrespective of the debatable nature of the face that accompanied it. This brain in turn does not conform to the status of the almost contemporary Sinanthropus. The human phylogeny, for all its general clarity in broad outline, is confused by spotty detail strewn over the giant land mass of Eurasia.

As we approach the present, we observe across the wastes of time a curious paradox. Man's physical likeness grows, but the brain takes many pathways and absorbs contrasting values. Cultural difference multiplies as the socialized ego departs further from the natural world into the realm of culture, which is its own creation. Those diversified monumental structures labeled "civilizations" have, throughout written history, risen and dissolved repeatedly. They have offered a variety of choices to man. They have been warlike or peaceful, optimistic or sad. Man has built and adapted to them all. Now, in the enormous centrifugal whirlpool of modern scientific technology, the entire human world is threatened by the pace of its own induced change.

Many distinct cultures and subcultures—our own included—show an increasing confusion of values. The one world we have talked about so glibly is increasingly a nightmare. Its cultural innovations are frequently turned outward in threat and counter-threat. Its massed regimentation is an increasing denial of all those qualities of transcendence that the word "human" invokes.

In closing this brief examination of the beginnings of that organ which in our time has wrought both unconscionable devastation and at the same time peered farther into the universe than any generation before it, I should like to conclude with a caution expressed by Einstein. "If I have learned anything from the speculations of a long life," he wrote, "it is that we are a much greater distance away from a deep insight into the elementary processes of Nature than most of my colleagues believe." If Einstein was willing to admit this of the physical world he studied, how much more seriously should his words be taken by those of us who seek to understand that volatile and elusive phenomenon known as life. Like a phantom, it eludes our pursuit. In the end it will depart from each of us, as long ago it faded from the eyes of an unnamed creature who almost 2 million years later would be called Homo habilis, "the clever one."

REFERENCES CITED

Beerbower, J. T., 1960, Search for the Past, Prentice-Hall, Inc., Englewood Cliffs, N.J. p. 187.

Hallowell, A. E., 1959, "Behavioral Evolution and the Emergence of the Self," in Evolution and Anthropology, Anthropological Society of Washington, Washington, D.C., p. 59.

Hockett, C. F., and R. Ascher, 1964, "The Human Revolution," Am. Scientist, 52, p. 72.

Howell, F. C., 1959, "The Villafranchian and Human Origins," Science, 130, p. 840.

Müller, F. M., 1891, Nature, 44, p. 430.

Page, Thornton, ed., 1962, Stars and Galaxies: Birth, Aging and Death in the Universe, Prentice-Hall, Inc., Englewood Cliffs, N.J., p. 18.

Washburn, S. L., and F. C. Howell, 1960, "Human Evolution and Culture," in Evolution After Darwin, Vol. 2 Sol Tax, ed., University of Chicago Press, Chicago, p. 45.

Watson, D. M. S., 1928, Paleontology and the Evolution of Man, Oxford University Press, New York, p. 27.

Brain, Behavior, and Slow Time

CHARLES D. ARING
Department of Neurology
University of Cincinnati College of Medicine
and the Cincinnati General Hospital

I AM not sure that my experience with patients and medical students qualifies me as an observer of primitive man. If, as Whitehead says, "The present contains all that there is," I may qualify, for the related concept that ontogeny recapitulates phylogeny enables us to recognize what may be primitive remnants in present populations, especially among the young. Individually, recapitulation offers us some reassurance with the thought that, as we age, we are evolving.

In my mind's eye I can see a primate deserting the trees, thereby freeing his rostral extremities for more abstract endeavor than climbing and swinging. I can watch him fall over his own feet, if he maneuvered them as infants do now. I understood the burgeoning elaborations of the fore-end of his neuraxis as primitive man began to fiddle with all and sundry, a trait that he has never relinquished. And I presume that the widespread fascination with Tarzan and his ilk is a bit of nostalgia.

Where my sight grows particularly dim, as seeing "through a glass, darkly" and knowing only in part, as the Apostle Paul said, is with the intricacies of behavior. I recognize the infant in modern man, in fact, I feel him in myself. The behavior of man's immediate ancestors is not to be discerned; behavior leaves no bones. But modern man furnishes us with plenty to contemplate in this regard.

What makes for a finely functioning nervous system and an admirable output as compared to the run of the mill? I venture that brains are our greatest waste product in a culture that has been fantastically wasteful. We all possess within our skulls this greatest mechanism known to man, a singular structure made up of billions of parts. In the majority of the world's living populations, the resultant of its functions is not a good deal more impressive than that which derives from the nervous system of the

flatworm. Yet the functioning of the flatworm's nervous system
is said to surpass that of our best electronic computers.

Attempts are continually launched to analyze the product of
the brain known as mind, each trial taking off from the investigator's small launching pad of security—thus "the chill physicochemical concept of the human mind," as Sir Francis Walshe (1953)
termed it in his critique. He drew the following proposition from
among some mechanistic formulations appearing in a monograph on
the cerebral cortex of man: "If the proper study of mankind is man,
surely the supreme biological interest of man is his brain, particularly the grey cortex of two billion cells without the orchestra-
tion of which there can be no thought, no sweet Sonnets of Shakespeare, no joy and no sorrow." Sir Francis's riposte was: "What
a typical materialist's half-truth! What a pregnant silence about
the other half, for, from the dumbest blonde to the wisest sage,
each of us has a quota of two billion grey cells, yet the human
race has produced but one Shakespeare."

There is the dilemma: why we do as we do with this uniquely
exquisite equipment. While the deviousness of blondes, especially
dumb ones, is not quite as baffling as the genius of Shakespeare, I
find it difficult to have any but the crudest notions about why people
behave the way they do. This may have to do with the impossible
task posed by a consideration of all the available evidence. So
much is impinging upon a person at any one time in his life that
to keep it all in view is not possible. The problem is compounded
when the survey is longitudinal. Our biases affect the selection
of material considered to be relevant etiologically. The data is
so lush that it is likely that the human mind, wonderful as it is,
cannot process it without the help of mechanical aids. Here we
might make good use of what Walshe, in his criticism of the
mechanists, termed "their electronic fairies," for with them,
we can keep the data to heel.

We are wary of correlating size of brain with quality. There is
evidence for a progressive increase in size of the brain during the
preceding million or millions of years, derived from measurements
of the skull capacity of fossil apes and men and of modern man.
However, the size of the brain varies exceedingly among all species
of modern Primates, and few if any correlations have been established for a normal population between brain weight and mental
capacity. Brain content between 800 and 2,200 cc has been regarded
as normal in man. The average skull capacity of American men
is about 1,450 cc, "A Litre and a Half of Brains" as Todd (1927)

and O'Leary (1963) entitled their studies of it. The brain of Anatole France was 1,017 or 1,100 cc, depending on the authority you read, not much more than the established capacity of Pithecan- thropus erectus, and that of Johnathan Swift was twice as capa- cious (2,200 cc), facts interesting but not understandable.

Nor can we yet equate other neural derivations with how a person behaves, except under the grossest of circumstances. The study of neuronal circuitry or chemistry, while fascinating and impor- tant, as yet tells us little about a person's "quality" or "style." It is now as it was about a century ago, when the senior Oliver Wendell Holmes remarked in an address before the Phi Beta Kappa Society of Harvard University (June 29, 1870): "We do not find Hamlet and Faust, right and wrong, the valor of men and the purity of women by...examining fibres in microscopes."

I subscribe to the proposition that there is nothing of greater complexity or interest in the universe than the human brain. We should continue to nudge this magnificent structure with every reasonable method, to encourage the revelation of its secrets, and to try to improve upon its uses. Historically, we believe that we see such an improvement, as we judge it, certainly from species to species of man's antecedents, and it is likely to have occurred over the eons in the creature termed Homo sapiens. But it must be kept in mind that perhaps more demand is put on the human brain, as constituted, in surviving a primitive en- vironment than in composing, say, Hamlet.

The developmental dilemma may be illustrated with a con- sideration of the laterality of modern man. Other evolutionary vestiges could also serve as examples. Man seems inordinately proud of being considered left-handed or ambidextrous. As it turns out, he is rarely left-handed and never ambidextrous. He may be ambisinistrous—in other words, coping with two left hands—which is likely to be related to a certain deviousness that has been impressed upon his brain.

The effects of man's confrontation with a world becoming right-sided must have been far reaching. As we strive to deter- mine man's development over the eons, we believe we see its milestones reflected in the infant handling himself and things indifferently. There is discernible the imprint of primitive and relatively automatic neural mechanisms as the baby moves. Children who are poorly endowed, as we say, may never develop a preferred laterality. Then they remain as ambilateral as we consider animals to be or Stone Age man to have been.

At about the age of nine months, the infant begins to favor one side of his body over the other. How this came about in prehistoric man is shrouded in "silence and slow time." Dextrality appears to hark back to the development of one-sided tools of some complexity in the Bronze Age. What dictated the choice of the right over the left, to result in this right-sided world, is an enigma. But once established, ethical and moral values have maintained it: good or righteous for the right, and bad or sinister or gauche for the left. Etymologic connotations are quite clear on this point in practically all languages, ancient and modern.

Today we see confusions in directional orientation reflected in many functions. Writing and reading disabilities and developmental motor awkwardness are cases in point, as is the mental problem. Besides motor ineptitude, these people tend to be tense, anxious, inhibited, introverted, and self-conscious. They suffer a mental directional disorientation, so to speak. It has been said that large discrepancies between verbal and performance scores in intelligence examinations may be considered characteristic of developmental motor awkwardness. Abram Blau (1946) characterizes this condition as a form of "motor stuttering," engendered by the fact that neither hand enjoys special learning opportunities, the child continuing in his original unskillfulness. The problem was known to Galen, who spoke of "ambilevous" children. The responsibility of environmental factors in this disorder is obvious to Blau who mentions the prime position of a negativistic type of emotional disturbance imposed by infantilization in relation to a neurotic mother. This clumsiness of unorganized motor capacities becomes more or less patterned in the nervous system during subsequent maturation.

I am not one to quarrel with the conception that the emotions have access to many bodily functions. We may derive information about etiological factors with ontological observation, and transpose it into hints about phylogeny. But the study of the individual is made difficult by the myriad and subtle effects of surroundings, which constantly bombard the organism from the day of conception. Even the observer of this human galaxy affects it by the mere fact of observing. The composition of my Mozart, or my Jefferson, or my Freud is what I make of their genius; such conceptions are idiosyncractic for each of us (Dorsey, 1965), despite the resemblances.

In the grand sweep of then and now, including the repository subsumed in the Jungian concept of the collective unconscious,

I find no reassuring answer in my quest for the reason for the ubiquity of neurosis, whose fearsomely wide range includes you and me. But the incidence of neurosis is to me not so ominous as the fact that it is fostered by the culture. Lawrence Kubie (1961) noted that human ingenuity has not yet devised a political or economic system that does not exploit, intensify, and reward much that is neurotic (potentially even psychotic) in human nature. He wonders what would happen to our economy if we were all to get well suddenly. The exploitation of neurosis by many cultural forces is bound to affect the neurotic process, and thus health.

It may be, as many have indicated (Breland, 1965; Harper, 1958, and MacLean, 1962), that we have frozen in situ a nervous system composed of reptilian, lower mammal, and late mammal parts, and at present are somewhat stuck with our emotional constitution. The American historian James Harvey Robinson (1863-1936) said as much in his Mind in the Making: "In the mind of man dwells the monkey, the savage, the baby and the civilized man, and the problem is for all of them to live in peace together." We know how evanescent is peace in human affairs. Although behavior has left behind no bones, as we observe modern man and particularly the infant in action, we see much that inevitably reminds us of the primitive. Perhaps, as Breland (1965, p. 17) has said, when the more-primitive parts of the nervous system "take over" from the cortex, so to speak, we see behavior not unlike the displacement activities of lower forms, as when two male sticklebacks about to fight go to the bottom of the aquarium to dig, making typical nest-building movements. Some gulls in their belligerency also go through nest-building patterns; others may seem to go to sleep. The narcolepsy syndrome in man is a reasonable facsimile of this last condition: a neurotic kind of peace that does not heal, or knit up the "ravell'd sleave of care." Behavior such as this is called regressive when it occurs in the human.

It seems reasonable to say that primitive parts of the central nervous system often gain the ascendancy in human affairs. Many poets have said so. The greatest of them has said of man, on the one hand: "How noble in reason!...in apprehension how like a god!...the paragon of animals!" and on the other:

> His glassy essence, like an angry ape,
> Plays such fantastic tricks before high heaven,
> As make the angels weep.

John Keats, who, it seems worth recalling, was a surgeon, wrote in a letter to his friend John Reynolds, "A man should have the fine point of his soul taken off to become fit for this world," and in another, written a few months later to his brothers George and Thomas, "There is nothing stable in the world; uproar's your only music." Along with the great physiologist Claude Bernard, and using his words, "I feel convinced that there will come a day when physiologists, poets and philosophers will all speak the same language and understand one another."

If neurosis may be called acting as though today were sometime past, I suppose it is reasonable to recognize the contribution of forebears to our lack of grace. This says nothing about responsibility, and surely does not license irresponsibility. We may imagine that when modern man is deprived of his full range of functions he may have to draw abruptly upon unbridled primitive capacities and function eccentrically. No doubt the energy bound to the past would reduce that available for current life needs. An analogy, though not an exact one, might be drawn to the man who has suffered an acute stroke, and who, until restitution occurs must rely on the parts of his brain that remain functional.

Many have wondered where this chain that links us so closely could be broken. Psychotherapy, useful though it is, hardly ripples the surface of the enormous problem. There is general commitment to busyness as a way of keeping out of trouble, and this is good. Perhaps methods of using the brain voluntarily could be devised so that there would be reduced opportunity for its devotion to lesser common denominators and to anachronism. Today we barely extend the uses of this marvelous organ.

There is evidence, derived from psychology, biochemistry, and anatomy, that change may be induced in the brain experimentally. It has been determined (Krech et al., 1960) that the brains of rats raised under conditions of environmental complexity and training—called environmental enrichment—when compared with those of isolated littermates used as controls, developed heavier cerebral cortices and were richer in the enzyme cholinesterase, which is involved in synaptic transmission. This might be considered the fallacy of largeness had it not been shown that environmentally enriched rats were superior in problem solving to their isolated littermates. Surely we believe that the brain may assess the probability that a message is important enough to be acted on by matching it against what has already been experienced. Experience is a substrate, and the nature of experience would seem crucial.

Thoreau looked upon the perception of beauty as a moral test, an idea also expressed in Rachel Carson's posthumous book (1965), "A Sense of Wonder." Shakespeare believed that a man is not to be trusted who "hath no music in himself, nor is not mov'd with concord of sweet sounds." An Arabian proverb of old says, "The eye is blind to what the mind does not see," which is akin to the statement of Horace that "A mind that is charmed by false appearances refuses better things." This same Roman succinctly outlined the prevailing carelessness with our greatest potentiality when he said: "If anything affects your eye, you hasten to have it removed; if anything affects your mind, you postpone the cure...." Perhaps as Heinrich Heine seemed to believe, it requires pain to move us away from apathy.

Fuller use of the capacities of the brain in man's quest for a clearer perception of his world can perhaps be made through the various creative arts—by mean of which man has, throughout history, brought forth and expressed a heightened awareness of truth and beauty and given voice to the "sense of wonder" that, perhaps more than anything else, distinguishes him from all other living creatures. Among the arts, poetry, which puts language to full use as both a stimulus and a tool for thought, exploration, and discovery, may be of particular help in this quest.

REFERENCES CITED

Blau, A., 1946, "The Master Hand, a Study of the Origin and Meaning of Right- and Left-Sidedness and Its Relation to Personality and Language," American Orthopsychiatric Association, Inc., New York, 206 pp.

Breland, M. K., 1965, "In Search of Adventure, A Letter to the Editor," Saturday Rev., Sept. 4, 48, 17.

Carson, R., 1965, The Sense of Wonder, Harper and Row, Publishers, Inc., New York, 89 pp.

Dorsey, J. M., 1965, Illness or Allness, Wayne State University Press, Detroit, 636 pp.

Harper, R. M. J., 1958, "Evolution and Illness," Lancet, ii, pp. 92-94.

Krech, D., M. R. Rosenzweig, and E. L. Bennett, 1960, Effects of Environmental Complexity and Training on Brain Chemistry, J. Comp. Physiol. Psychol., 53, 509-519.

Kubie, L. S., 1961, "The Eagle and the Ostrich," Arch. Gen. Psychiat., 5, 109-119.

MacLean, P. D., 1962, "New Findings Relevant to the Evolution of Psychosexual Functions of the Brain," J. Nervous Mental Disease, 135, 289-301.

O'Leary, J. L., 1963, "A Litre and a Half of Brains," Arch. Neurol., 8, 128-144.

Todd, T. W., 1927, "A Litre and a Half of Brains," Science, 46, 122-125.

Walsche, F., 1953, "Thoughts upon the Equation of Mind with Brain," Brain, 76, 1-18.

Time, Strata, and Fossils:
Comments and Recommendations

GLENN L. JEPSEN
Princeton University

T HIS SYMPOSIUM, focused by diversely oriented specialists
on the broad and controversial (and occasionally nebulous)
subjects of time and strata in the record of human evolution, has
offered no exception to the generality that many of the statements
planned by the final speaker for such a discussion have been well
said by the other participants before his turn comes to speak.
Fortunately, a few areas are left for new comment or for emphasis by repetition; and the fact that the attention of the symposium has been largely and necessarily directed to the re-
examination of well-known materials leads me to make a final
emphatic recommendation.

We have been examining modern man as the current stage in
human evolution and have considered some of the temporal, physical, and cultural events of his relatively recent past. Pertinent
generalities about primates may be derived also by looking at a
much earlier stage of Primate evolution, at some of the oldest
known forms from rocks of early Tertiary age in the time zone of
about 50 to 60 million years ago. Primate remains are among the
commoner fossils in fluviatile sediments of the mid-Paleocene
epoch in some parts of the western United States but are very
rare in older rocks. Thus, if we rely upon evidence from Wyoming,
Montana, and New Mexico we see a sudden origin, or explosion,

of new taxa of "primitive" Primates in Torrejonian time. Quite
clearly the apparent suddenness of this taxonomic blast is an
artifact of ignorance: primate diversification had undoubtedly
been progressing for a very long time.

These records of early Primates, congealed in solid rock
and extremely difficult to find and to read, provide the significant information that the modes of evolution of Primates, the
kinds of genetic change, were probably no different then from now,
and that the complex products of phylogeny are the constantly
selected increments of continuous similar processes. This apparent fact is especially noted by vertebrate paleontologists as
they trace the parallel sequences in the family lines of ancient
petrified Primates upward through horizon upon horizon of the
chronolithic record. In genealogies such as those, for example,
that ascend through sequences of many strata in the Bighorn
Basin of Wyoming, representing the passage of several million
years, we see irregularities in the directions and speeds of
transformation in evolving lines of proto-lemur-like creatures.
Various groups climb the rock ladder of time with differing
speeds of morphic change, and some exemplify on a grand scale
parallelisms such as those perceived by Dr. Robinson among the
African euhominids.

It is unfortunate that most of our old fossil ancestors have
come through time to us only in the form of small fragments.
The records we read in these petrified particles are like irregu-
lar and infrequent stroboscopic flashes that are far too brief to
illuminate all we would like to see.

Unfortunately, also, for observers who want nature to be tidy
and regular, the rungs of the temporal ladder that we perceive
are not equally spaced. Some fossil-yielding strata represent
time periods that were close together. Others represent widely
separated intervals, and the corresponding gaps in the fossil
record are occupied by the kinds of human inference and predic-
tion that have often been proved wrong by the discovery of new
specimens.

After the title of this symposium was proposed by Dr. Wolman
and it was obvious that geologic time would be a major consideration for this assembly, I asked several thoughtful scientists,
"What is time ?" No two gave the same answer. "Time is change."
"Time is a measured distance between events." "Time is en-
tropy." "Time is a comparison of processes." "Time is when."
Abstractly, time in the evolution of man is presumably like time

in the evolution of early Primates and like any other time; but, to recall some frequently forgotten truisms, the paleoanthropologist in his search for the proper sequences of events must depend upon knowledge about the relative positions of fossils in rock strata, or upon geochemical revelations about "absolute" time, or upon assumptions about rates and kinds of processes, such as morphologic and cultural change. Some assumptions about the pace of physical and mental evolution are notoriously untrustworthy. Without information from stratigraphy or geochemistry, who knows which of two forms of fossil man was first?

If we could have looked at segments of our phylogeny from the opposite direction of time, from earlier places along the ascent, many of the guesses about future priority would have been equally vague. At no time in man's past since he became a primate (or even a "people-directed prebiologic blob") could anyone have predicted, with all the most sophisticated information that we have now about evolutionary processes and directions, the shape or intelligence of distant descendants. Neither the discarded theory of orthogenesis nor its replacing theory of ortho-selection could ever have served as compasses to indicate the direction of the future; they point the way only in our retrospective inquiries.

Unfortunately, we cannot depend upon uniformity in the rate of evolution to generate such unique human qualities as body configuration or brain size. When we were australopithecines, as previous speakers have said we were, we had modern subcranial bodies and rather archaic microbrained heads. Between that time and now, as our average total bulk increased about 50 percent our endocranial volume became 300 percent larger. Before the evidences of these disparate rates within man's makeup were recognized, several generations of fossil interpreters had assumed that human heads and bodies had developed apace at uniform rates of change.

Another excellent case of eccentricity of rates is now known (or at least believed) in the evolution of bats, an example that might be said to have historical pertinence to the development of ideas about man's relatives and thus to the present discussion, because, more than 200 years ago, Linnaeus classified Vespertilio, the only bat he knew, as one of the four genera of Primates. If the remarkably complete skeleton of a 50-million-year-old early Eocene bat from Wyoming (No. 18150, Princeton Museum of Natural History) were to be clothed in muscles and skin, it would

appear in flight to be a modern bat. Most observers would see
nothing unusual about its anatomy or its fluttering flight. At the
time it actually lived, the contemporary horses were fox-sized
polydactyls and apparently our own ancestral galaxy of genes
had produced nothing beyond a small lemur-like phenotype.

Actually, if all bats were people-sized we would see many
minor differences between the hypothetically resurrected early
Tertiary bat and modern bats. If a generalized estimate is made
of the speed of bat evolution (expressed, perhaps, in darwins)
between the time of this earliest-known flying mammal and the
present, and if this rate is then extended back to the time when
the forebears of bats were terrestrial or arboreal insectivore-
like animals, a point would be reached in geologic time well
within or even before the Paleozoic Era. The significant lesson
of this splendid absurdity is that evolutionary rates have varied
widely within a phylum. A similar structure - time nonsense
extrapolation of rate, from size of brain of modern man back to
that of australopithecines and beyond, would reach the brain size
of a small lemur in only a few million years.

Over an early Tertiary fossil, consisting of small cranial
fragments and an endocranial cast in clay, Dr. Tilly Edinger and
I have sustained a friendly controversy for many years. Unfortunately the tooth-bearing parts of the specimen are missing.
The "braincase" clearly shows that the posterior or acoustic
colliculi of the midbrain were larger than the anterior (sight
associated) pair, a size relationship that is seen in most of the
bats that practice echolocation. To Dr. Edinger these facts indicate that the little fossil is a bat. The bony structures, however,
appear to indicate miacid carnivore relationships. Some small
miacid contemporaries (with teeth preserved) also had the same
relative sizes of colliculi and hence may have had advanced techniques for audioresponse, as do living cetaceans and certain birds
and insectivores. Perhaps this ability was formerly more widespread than it is at present. No one knows when it began in bats or
in any other animal.

To paleoneurologists the configurations of human and other
cranial endocasts reveal many characteristics of the living brain.
The skull, however, invests not only the brain but the tissues
around it as well and is hence not an exact mold of the brain.
And, of course, no void in a fossilized humanoid head can indicate
the state of intelligence, or of technologic conceptualization, or
of humanity that resided there. The brain's bony box is like a
purse: contents are more significant than size or shape.

Another primary geologic concept merits emphasis. In order to talk about relative times of processes and products in the evolution of man, we must, as Dr. Hay has done in his lucid discussion of the strata at Olduvai, divide geologic time into "chronologic units" that are based upon such occurrences as the deposition of a stratum of sediment, and try to match the times of these events from place to place. This is a difficult, tedious, and frustrating exercise. Dr. Hay, properly cautious, is yet unwilling to propose correlations of the rocks at Olduvai with those of approximately similar age in Europe. And who knows what was happening to affect man's existence in other parts of the world?

Many of the early notions about strata were based upon studies of consolidated marine sediments, and some of these ideas were unfortunately carried over into investigations of terrestrial sediments. The boundaries between blocks of time were deliberately set in the places where the records were weakest—at the points in chronology where a group of organisms or several groups apparently began or ended or where there was clearly some other kind of break or hiatus in the records. Now, with greater sophistication, we realize that the best place to establish a necessarily arbitrary rock - time boundary would be somewhere within a single widespread zone or formation of rock that contained abundant fossils of many kinds of animals and plants. A clock that skips no intervals is more satisfactory than one that jumps across some of time's minutes or millennia.

Citing the extinction of dinosaurs as the chronologic marker for the end of the Cretaceous Period is operationally rather useful but highly inexact. Which dinosaur died last, and when, and where?

Anthropologists are often targets for the apparently simple question, "When did the first species of man live?" This causes the harassed professionals to reach for a definition of man, and they seem to have come to several definitions that are based more upon what man's ancestors did than upon their physical attributes. Man may be defined as "the creature that uses tools, which he fabricates in repeated designs" if we ignore the thresholds of tool-using by great apes, sea otters, woodpecker-finches, and wasps. We may confidently predict today, however, that variations of the proposition, "Resolved that the great Pleistocene growth of man's brain was an adaptive (non-Lamarckian) morphological response to his development of technology," will continue to be debated for a long time. The wise and

beautifully designed statements by Dr. Eiseley will help clarify
the issues in homogenesis. Man, like other animals, evolves as
an element of an ecologic whole that includes his social and
mental attributes.

To the vertebrate paleontologists, who habitually see man's
history in vast perspective, there never was a first man or a
first primate; the billions of genetic filaments in our ancestral
phyletic cord are of many lengths, no two precisely the same.
We have not had our oversized brain very long, but the penta-
dactyl pattern of our extremities originated deep in our Paleozoic
amphibian condition. It is possible to think of some genes or
loci or cistrons as short-lived, of others as being extremely
durable in the biochemical forebears of man. Obviously the
relationship of anatomic characters to genetic stuffs is even
less determinable in extinct than in extant man.

And, of course, the popular "biological definition" of a species
as being "a group of potentially interbreeding natural populations
that are reproductively isolated from other such groups" is often
reduced to nonsense when attempts are made to apply it to fossils.
Even among most living nonhuman forms it is not susceptible to
rigorous test. By this definition all the members of a monophy-
letic group and all the branches of a single family tree, no matter
how long it has been evolving or how complex it has become,
belong to a single species.

Each genetic lineage of mammals is composed at every moment
in time of individuals of differing ages and overlapping life spans.
No species in a genetic cord can be "reproductively isolated"
from its immediate ancestors or from its immediate descendants.
It is virtually a genetic continuum in which there are no gaps.
The one sine qua non about such a sequence of "species" is that
there has not been reproductive isolation, or distinctly different
adjacent members of the line, and any system that treats segments of the continuum as separate entities for the sake of con-
venience is simply avoiding the problems of trying to express
thoughts about phylogenies and about ways to describe sequences
of morphic grades. Words like "adaptation" and "species" may be
used to conceal as well as to reveal ideas and observations.

Only when we abstract a wholly artificial and thin horizontal
slice from a family tree can the biological definition of species
be applied, and then only to living forms, not to the vast majority
of fossil taxa that are known now or to the even greater number
that will assuredly be discovered in the future.

Some thoughtful biologists regard the effort to find actual models to fit the biological definition of species as a curious example of displacement activity among taxonomists, because the search for uniform and universally applicable concepts of species is so futile. What, then, can we call a species among the 99 percent of organisms that are now defunct ? An impeccable and commonly applied definition is given by Ehrlich and Holm in The Process of Evolution (1963, p. 330), as "a group of organisms judged by taxonomists (by diverse criteria) to be worthy of formal recognition as a distinct kind."

This or any other definition will do little to resolve the routine squabbles among nomenclators as long as they gain prestige by naming taxa. Some taxonomists have consistently urged the recognition of at least two major kinds or concepts of classification. One of these, sometimes referred to as phenetic classification, is based entirely upon appearance or morphologic attributes. The other kind, which most of the speakers today have had in mind, is erected upon assumptions about genealogic relationships and is called phyletic classification. Obviously no static taxonomic system yet devised can perfectly represent any dynamic process of evolution, but the pretense that it can is a common functional fiction among the hopeful manipulators of names of species. Equally obvious is the fact, repeated for emphasis, that in the study of arrays of fossils we must base the criteria for species almost entirely upon appearances—upon phenetic qualities rather than upon assumptions about phyletic factors. Many expressions of concern are engendered by the recent squabbles that have attended the christening ceremonies as the new fossil hominids have been plucked from their natal beds of African rocks. For this taxonomic chatter around the baptismal fonts a third category of classification, the phrenetic, may be suggested.

These comments are leading to my first recommendation: for perceiving and naming species, anthropologists should practice the relatively objective systems and codified rules that competent specialists use for the classification of nonhominid groups. Even the best procedure for judging what reasonably constitutes a dead species, which is represented only by bones and teeth, is often inexact and nebulous, but it can avoid the emotional attitude that an anthropologist (now deceased) displayed when he refused to synonymize one name of a fossil hominid with another name only "because I am very fond of the beautiful specimen; it is a part of me." Such a personalized nomenclatural whim is a feeble vehicle for communication; and it equates a species to one animal instead of to a group.

Another imaginitive writer refused to examine a proffered array of early Tertiary fossil primates because he preferred to "get ideas from thinking about remote origins." And in this way some specialists boldly go far out on limbs of their own devising on the family tree.

G. G. Simpson (1963, p. 5), in discussing the chaotic status of anthropological nomenclature, comments that, "Insofar as the chaos is due to faulty linguistics rather than to zoological dis-agreements, it stems either from ignorance or from refusal to follow rules and usages. This must be almost the only field in science in which those who do not know and follow the estab-lished norms have so frequently had the temerity and opportunity to publish research that is, in this respect, incompetent."

We need many more hominoid fossils. To the bored sophomore who asks, "Good Lord, do we have to learn all those ?", we seem to have more than an adequate number of prehuman bone frag-ments with which to grow and climb a strong and wholly satis-factory family tree, but to the specialist the grafts of many of the branches in the genealogic charts of human evolution seem too weak to support the weight of ascent. Dr. Pecora has com-mented that the general growth pattern of man's family tree has not been greatly altered by recent discoveries and that the desirability of securing and organizing more information should be emphasized. At best, arboriculture seems to be a slow enter-prise in anthropology.

And, to the dismay of paleontologists some neontologists still persist in the naive practice of drawing "family trees" that are based solely upon the morphologic attributes of living species, sometimes even ignoring known fossil forms. This manipulation is not much more meaningful biologically than the exercise of arraying the bottles in a junk shop in "genealogies" on the basis of differences of color and shape and size.

Students also often ask what percentage of all the Primates in the line that led to man are known as fossils. Obviously there are too many unknowns to attempt an adequately informed answer. Each little nervously chattering primate that lived in Paleocene time presumably had some chance of being represented now by at least part of its skeleton in some museum's collection of fossils. What were the odds ? An unsatisfactory but informative

calculation can be made. After death, only one carcass in perhaps a thousand (to guess conservatively) was not eaten by pred-
ators or scavengers and was buried before the bones disinte-
grated; of those that were enclosed in sediments, only one in,
say, ten became petrified, and these may have had about the same
chance (one in ten) of withstanding dissolution by underground
water. What were the chances that a survivor of all these
vicissitudes would be exposed later by erosion or some other
means in such a place and at such a time that someone with
requisite knowledge and skill and resources and motive would
find it and take it to a museum ? One chance in one hundred
thousand is a very liberal estimate. Combine these odds and
the museum expectation of an early Tertiary lemur is about 1 in
10 billion. Even at this low residue rate, still remaining in the
rocks are many thousands of early Primate specimens that may
be found and studied in future research.

These feebly based guesses about numbers of fossils lead
to a strong final recommendation: Do more field research and
find more ancient hominid fossils! There are many of these
fossils, entombed in sediments in various parts of the Old World,
that will ultimately come to light. Their debut can be hastened
without excessive cost or effort. Only their study can provide
the requisite objective data for future decisions about man's
growing past. (Future knowledge of man's skeletal framework
is secure—no other mammal approaches him in the fraction of
his bony biomass that will be preserved, through his present
interment practices, hereafter.) Additional fossils are required
not only to extend our information about them but to integrate
what we already know about our ancient selves. We literally
need more spade work in anthropology; we shall have to extend
the digging with pick and shovel before we can progress much
further with pencil and paper.

A manifold increase of searching and digging for the past in
the lithobiosphere is clearly indicated if we are to resolve some
of the persistant problems of time and stratigraphy in the evolution of man. More materials and more wisdom are needed in
order that (to literalize Tennyson) "men may rise on stepping-
stones of their dead selves to higher things."